Building with atoms

D0346311

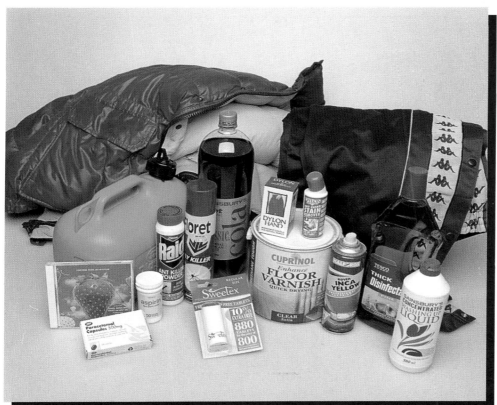

8

Photo on title page   Some examples of the wide range of products that are made starting from compounds that are found in crude oil.

The Open University, Walton Hall, Milton Keynes MK7 6AA

First published 1998

Written, edited, designed and typeset by the Open University.

Printed and bound in the United Kingdom by Jarrold Book Printing, Norfolk, England.

ISBN 0 7492 8194 4

This text forms part of an Open University course, S103 *Discovering Science*. The complete list of texts that make up this course can be found on the back cover. Details of this and other Open University courses can be obtained from the Course Reservations and Sales Office, PO Box 724, The Open University, Milton Keynes MK7 6ZS, United Kingdom: tel. (0044) 1908 653231.

For availability of this or other course components, contact Open University Worldwide Ltd, The Berrill Building, Walton Hall, Milton Keynes MK7 6AA, United Kingdom: tel. (00 44) 1908 858585, fax (00 44) 1908 858787, e-mail ouwenq@open.ac.uk. Alternatively, much useful course information can be obtained from the Open University's website http://www.open.ac.uk

s103block8i1.1

Contents

Introduction

In the first half of S103, *Discovering Science*, the world was taken apart. As part of that theme, we entered the microscopic world of atoms in Block 6, and then showed how all atoms could be taken apart into protons, neutrons and electrons. We continued the process in Block 7 by showing how protons, neutrons and electrons could be either classified as, or further broken up into, quarks or leptons.

Here in Block 8, we start the second half of S103, in which the world will be put back together. This is not just a reversal of course! In taking the world apart, we have learnt much about the particles of which things are made. So we are now in a better position to understand how the world works as we build it up again from fragments such as hadrons, leptons or atoms that we identified in the first half of the course. Indeed, this whole process is so important that there is a special word for it; it is called *reductionism*: the attempt to explain the behaviour of something by drawing attention to the combined actions of its component parts.

Just how deeply we delve into the structure of things when we do this will depend on the problem to hand. Sometimes it will be convenient to start an explanation at the level of atoms; at others with protons, neutrons and electrons. Here, in Block 8, the latter is the case.

The material in Block 8 is arranged into three distinct topics. In Sections 2 to 5, we apply our understanding of the structure of atoms to categorize and predict the properties of compounds. In one of the crowning moments of the early part of the block, you will see how the Periodic Table of Block 6 is a consequence of the way in which the electrons in atoms are arranged about the nucleus. The general term that we shall use for this arrangement is **electron structure**.

In Sections 6 to 11 we concentrate on the features of chemical reactions, the energy changes associated with reactions, how we can control the amounts of products formed and how fast reactions proceed. This provides the basis for understanding how many important industrial processes work.

In the last part of the block (Sections 12–17) we examine how all this chemistry can be applied. Our topic is crude oil and its uses. This introduces us to a major aspect of chemistry, the chemistry of carbon compounds, and it involves a study of fuels, plastics and pharmaceuticals. All life is based on carbon compounds and thus this section provides the link between the chemistry and physics you have studied in Blocks 5, 6, 7 and 8 and the biology that you will meet in Block 9.

While studying Block 8 you will be building on the knowledge gained from earlier blocks. You will be re-using skills you have already developed, such as designing experimental work, classifying, problem solving, critical reading and how to construct a logical argument, and thus seeing how they transfer to a new context.

Electrons in atoms: a look forward and a look back

The atom that emerged from Block 6 was a tiny, positively charged nucleus surrounded by electrons. Then, in Block 7 Section 4, you found out how those surrounding electrons are arranged in the three simplest types of atom — those of hydrogen, helium and lithium. Now, in Block 8, we extend this study of electron arrangement to many other atoms. Those arrangements are of special importance for the science of chemistry. In Section 3, for example, they explain the shape of the Periodic Table; in Section 5, they explain why hydrogen and oxygen react to form water, H_2O, and not HO or HO_2.

Put simply, the essential idea is that the electrons are arranged in *shells*, but this language must be moderated because of the strange behaviour of electrons that was discussed in Block 7. Consider argon, which has atomic number 18.

⬤ What is the positive charge on the nucleus of the argon atom, and how many electrons surround that nucleus?

◯ The atomic number is equal to the number of units of positive charge on the nucleus. This charge is therefore $+18e$. Because the atom is neutral, and each electron carries a single unit of negative charge, $-e$, there must be 18 surrounding electrons.

From Block 7 Section 3.4.1, you know that we cannot say exactly where an electron in an atom will be at any moment; we can speak only of the *probability* of finding an electron at a particular point. However, let us not be deterred by this. Think of an argon atom as a tiny sphere. Imagine starting at the centre (the nucleus) and moving outwards, seeking an electron at each distance from the nucleus as you go. Figure 2.1 does for argon what Figure 3.5 of Block 7 does for hydrogen: it shows the calculated distances at which the probability of finding an electron in an argon atom is at a maximum. There are three of them.

⬤ What are these three distances?

◯ About 5 pm, 20 pm and 70 pm.

We can describe this situation by saying that the 18 electrons in an argon atom are arranged in three **shells**. These shells are regions where the probability of finding an electron is especially high. Alternatively, and more usefully, you can think of them as regions where, over an extended period, the electrons spend most of their time. Shells are numbered 1, 2, 3, ... etc. as we move outward from the nucleus. In Block 7, this number was called the principal quantum number, and given the symbol n.

From Block 7, however, you know something more: the shells of electrons can be divided into sub-shells. It turns out that the number of sub-shells in any shell is equal to the principal quantum number of that shell. The first sub-shell in a shell is given the symbol s; if there is a second, it is given the symbol p; if a third, the symbol d, and if a fourth the symbol f. So a sub-shell can be identified by writing down the principal quantum number of its shell, followed by its characteristic letter. Thus, the f sub-shell of the shell of principal quantum number 4 is written 4f. Let's consider the shells with principal quantum numbers 1 and 2.

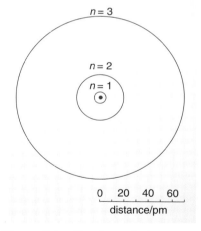

Figure 2.1 The three circles identify three distances from the nucleus of an argon atom at which the probability of finding an electron is at a maximum ($1 \text{ pm} = 1 \text{ picometre} = 10^{-12} \text{ m}$). These distances mark the existence of three shells with principal quantum numbers 1, 2 and 3.

How many sub-shells are these shells divided into, and what symbol will each sub-shell be given?

There is one sub-shell in the shell with $n = 1$, so this will be given the symbol s. In the shell with $n = 2$, there will be two sub-shells, so these will be given the symbols s and p. Thus the sub-shells can be written 1s, 2s and 2p.

The sub-shells will form the core of our description of the arrangement of electrons in an atom. This is because that arrangement can be represented by an **electron configuration**, which tells us what sub-shells are occupied, and how many electrons there are in each one.

Electron configurations

3

The electron configuration of an atom is obtained by writing down the occupied sub-shells, and specifying the number of electrons in each one by a superscript number. Consider, for example, atoms of hydrogen, helium and lithium, which contain 1, 2 and 3 electrons, respectively. In Block 7, you learnt that the electron configurations of these three atoms are $1s^1$, $1s^2$ and $1s^2 2s^1$. The electron configurations of the hydrogen atom, $1s^1$, and the helium atom, $1s^2$, tell us that the hydrogen atom contains just one electron in the 1s sub-shell, and the helium atom contains two (Figure 3.1).

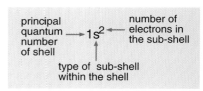

What does the electron configuration of the lithium atom ($1s^2 2s^1$) tell us?

That in the lithium atom, both the 1s and 2s sub-shells are occupied; the former contains two electrons and the latter one.

Figure 3.1 The symbolism used to identify a sub-shell and its electron content.

This raises two questions. First, why can't the three electrons of the lithium atom all go in the 1s sub-shell? The answer was provided in Block 7 Section 4.3: there is an upper limit on the number of electrons that each sub-shell can hold. Each sub-shell has its own quantum number, l, and for s, p, d and f sub-shells, this second quantum number takes the values 0, 1, 2 and 3, respectively. The quantum theory tells us that the maximum number of electrons for each sub-shell is equal to $2(2l + 1)$.

What values does this number take for s, p, d and f sub-shells?

The values are $2[(2 \times 0) + 1] = 2$, $2[(2 \times 1) + 1] = 6$, $2[(2 \times 2) + 1] = 10$, and $2[(2 \times 3) + 1] = 14$, respectively.

So in s, p, d and f sub-shells, there can be no more than 2, 6, 10 and 14 electrons, respectively. These limits, and other quantum rules from this section, are summarized in Figure 3.2. What they tell us is that at helium, where the electron configuration is $1s^2$, the 1s sub-shell is full. When, with lithium, a third electron must be accommodated, it must go into a new sub-shell (2s).

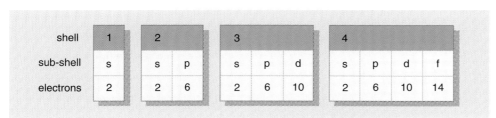

Figure 3.2 The sub-shells in the shells of principal quantum numbers 1–4, and the maximum number of electrons that each type of sub-shell can hold.

The second question is this: why, as we move from hydrogen, through helium, to lithium, is the 1s sub-shell occupied before the 2s? The answer is that the arrangement of the electrons in an atom is usually that of lowest energy, an arrangement known as the **ground state**. Now the lower energy states of atoms are those in which the negatively charged electrons spend more time closer to the positively charged nucleus, and in general, the lower the principal quantum number of a shell, the closer to the nucleus are its electrons likely to be found. This was also the message of Figure 2.1. Thus occupation of the 1s rather than the 2s sub-shell sets the electrons, and therefore the atom as a whole, in lower energy states, and this occupation continues until the 1s sub-shell is full. Only then does occupation of the 2s sub-shell begin.

During this argument, we have slipped in a rather subtle idea: the idea that the energy of an atom can be thought about in terms of the energies of its occupied sub-shells. One sub-shell has a lower energy than another if the electrons in it spend more time closer to the nucleus. The ground state of an atom is achieved by putting as many of its electrons as possible into the low-energy sub-shells. Let's apply this idea to the atoms beyond lithium.

3.1 Building atoms

We have just seen how we might write down the electron configuration of the atom of any element. The atomic number tells us the number of electrons in the atom. For lithium, this is three. We allocate these electrons to sub-shells, starting with the sub-shell of lowest energy. This sub-shell is 1s, and when two of the three electrons have been allocated to it, it is full. We then look for the sub-shell of next highest energy. This is 2s, and it takes the third electron: the electron configuration of lithium is $1s^2 2s^1$.

Figure 3.3 The order of ascending energy for the sub-shells that are occupied by electrons in the atoms with atomic numbers 1–20.

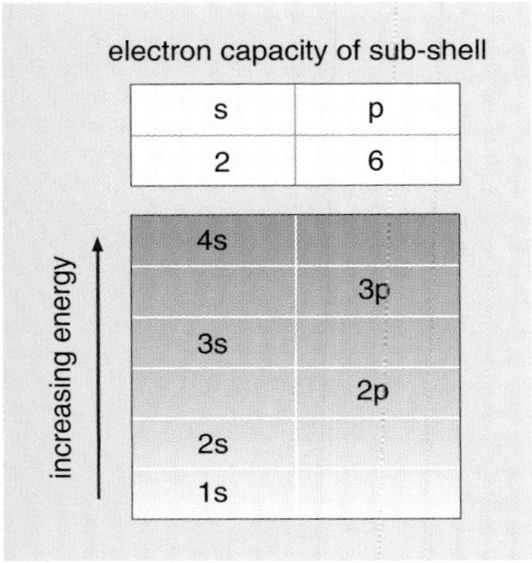

To apply this procedure beyond lithium, we need one more piece of information. *This is a diagram displaying all the relevant sub-shells in order of increasing energy.* Happily, electron configurations can be correctly assigned to *nearly all* atoms using just one such diagram. Figure 3.3 shows the early part of it, which is sufficient for the first 20 elements. Figure 3.4 shows these elements, with their atomic numbers, in a periodic table. Let's work out the electron configurations of their atoms.

						1 H	2 He
3 Li	4 Be	5 B	6 C	7 N	8 O	9 F	10 Ne
11 Na	12 Mg	13 Al	14 Si	15 P	16 S	17 Cl	18 Ar
19 K	20 Ca						

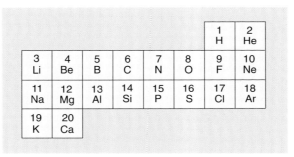

Figure 3.4 The first 20 elements in the Periodic Table.

The bottom of Figure 3.3 tells us what we already know: the sub-shell of lowest energy is 1s, followed by 2s. After lithium comes beryllium with atomic number 4.

- What is the electron configuration of the beryllium atom?

- $1s^2 2s^2$; the beryllium atom contains four electrons, and the first two go into the 1s sub-shell. This is now full, so the remaining two electrons go into the sub-shell of next highest energy; this is 2s.

After beryllium comes boron with atomic number 5.

- Is the electron configuration of the boron atom $1s^2 2s^3$?

- No; as an s sub-shell, the 2s sub-shell cannot contain more than two electrons (Figure 3.2). The fifth electron must occupy the sub-shell of next higher energy. Figure 3.3 shows us that this is 2p. Thus the electron configuration of the boron atom is $1s^2 2s^2 2p^1$.

Now, as we move beyond the boron atom, there is further filling of the 2p sub-shell.

● What will be the electron configuration of the first element with an atom in which the 2p sub-shell is full, and which element is it?

○ A p sub-shell is full when it contains six electrons (Figure 3.2), so the electron configuration will be $1s^2 2s^2 2p^6$. This contains 10 electrons in all, so the chemical element has an atomic number of 10. This is neon (Ne).

Activity 3.1   Working out the electron configurations of atoms 1–20

In this activity, you will produce a complete set of electron configurations for the first 20 elements. ◄

3.2   Explaining the Periodic Table

The essential idea behind the Periodic Table of Block 6 is that some elements are much more similar than others. The electron configurations of atoms might provide an explanation of this. In chemical reactions, atoms change their surroundings, and sometimes their surrounding atoms. We know that the outsides of atoms consist of electrons, so contact and connection between atoms is likely to take place through their *outer* electrons, that is, those electrons that spend more time farther out from the nucleus than the others. *So similarities in the arrangement of the outer electrons around two different types of atom may well lead to similarities in the chemistry of the two elements in question.* Let's see if there is any truth in this idea by turning to the alkali metals.

● Which of the first 20 elements are alkali metals?

○ Lithium, sodium and potassium, the elements in the first column of Figure 3.4.

From Activity 3.1, the electron configurations of these three atoms are:

Li $1s^2 2s^1$

Na $1s^2 2s^2 2p^6 3s^1$

K $1s^2 2s^2 2p^6 3s^2 3p^6 4s^1$

● What similarity exists between the last occupied sub-shells of these three configurations?

○ In each case it is an s sub-shell containing one electron.

The fact that the similarity is rooted in the nature and population of the last occupied sub-shell is very important. We have filled the sub-shells in order of increasing energy, so the electrons in this sub-shell are those of highest energy in the atom under consideration.

● What does this tell you, in general, about their distance from the nucleus?

○ As noted in Section 2, they are likely to be the electrons which, on average, spend their time farther from the nucleus than others; that is, they are outer electrons.

Thus the atoms of the similar elements lithium, sodium and potassium show a similarity in *outer* electron configuration. They all have an outer sub-shell of the type ns^1, where n is the principal quantum number of the outer shell. And this similarity in outer electron configuration leads to similarities in chemistry.

Question 3.1   Two other sets of elements that were shown to be similar in Block 6 were the metals of Group II, beryllium, magnesium and calcium, and the noble gases, neon and argon, which form no chemical compounds. Examine the electron configurations of these five atoms determined in Activity 3.1. What types of outer electron configuration do they have? Do these outer electron configurations show the expected similarities? ◄

So as we move from element to element in order of increasing atomic number, the electron configurations of the atoms show a *periodic variation*: elements with similar outer electron configurations appear at regular intervals. As the outer electrons of an atom have a strong influence on the chemistry of the element, this periodicity in outer electron configuration leads to a periodicity in the chemical properties of the elements. We have obtained a general explanation of chemical periodicity.

> The groups of similar elements that appear in columns in our Periodic Table have atoms with similar outer electron configurations.

Figure 3.5 summarizes how we have arrived at this conclusion.

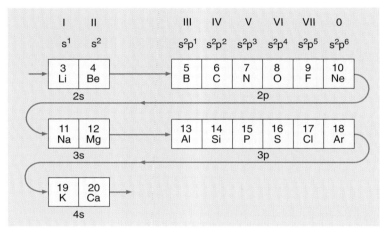

Figure 3.5   The winding arrowed pathway shows how the order of sub-shell energy and filling in Figure 3.3 generates the Periodic Table of Figure 3.4. Hydrogen and helium have been omitted (Section 3.2.1). Below the group numbers are the electron configurations of the occupied sub-shells in the outer shell of the atom. For the first row of Figure 3.5, the principal quantum number, n, of this outer shell is 2; for the second row it is 3, and for the third it is 4. Similar elements in the same column have similar outer sub-shell configurations.

3.2.1   Hydrogen and helium in the Periodic Table

There are two elements in the Periodic Table whose behaviour violates this simple idea. They are the first two: hydrogen and helium. The helium atom has the electron configuration $1s^2$. This suggests that it should be placed above beryllium in Group II. But this would make no chemical sense, because helium is a noble gas, and the Group II elements are reactive metals with valency two. This, then, is a case where similarity in outer electron configuration does not lead to similarities in chemical behaviour. As the Periodic Table is about chemistry, rather than just outer electron configurations, helium is placed above the other noble gases even though they have outer sub-shell configurations of the type np^6.

With hydrogen, things are less clear cut. In Block 6, the chemistry of hydrogen led us to classify it with the elements fluorine and chlorine in Group VII. But its electron configuration, $1s^1$, suggests that it should be classified with the alkali metals in Group I. Although hydrogen differs greatly from these very reactive metals, it does, like them, have a valency of one, and form an aqueous ion with a single positive charge. Because of these ambiguous properties, hydrogen is often not included in the main body of the Periodic Table. And we too shall sometimes omit it when we use the table in Sections 4 and 5.

3.3 An electronic tour of the Periodic Table

In Section 3.2, we built up the atoms of the first 20 elements using Figure 3.3. This exercise revealed a periodicity in outer electron configurations that matched the periodicity in chemical properties that is expressed by the mini Periodic Table of Figure 3.4. Can we do the same thing for the *complete* Periodic Table of the elements?

First we shall need the extended version of Figure 3.3. This is shown in Figure 3.6. It leads to the order of sub-shell filling shown in Figure 3.7. Now we can go beyond element 20 (calcium) and see if there is a periodicity in electron configuration that matches the full Periodic Table in Figure 12.6 of Block 6. We start where Figure 3.4 leaves off, at calcium. There, as Activity 3.1 showed, the 4s sub-shell is full. The next element is scandium, with atomic number 21.

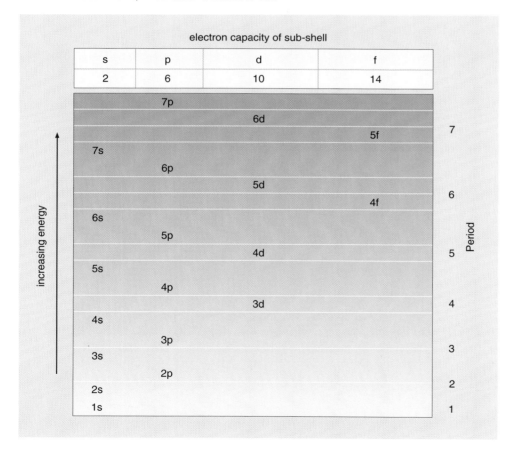

Figure 3.6 The order of ascending energy for the sub-shells that are occupied by electrons when we build up the atoms of all of the known chemical elements.

Figure 3.7 The arrowed pathway shows the order of filling generated by Figure 3.6.

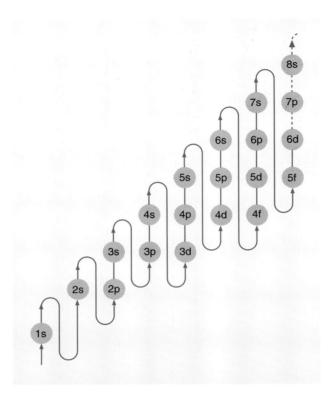

○ What new sub-shell begins to be filled in the scandium atom?

○ The 3d sub-shell; Figure 3.7 shows that occupation of this sub-shell begins when 4s is full. The electron configuration of the scandium atom is $1s^2 2s^2 2p^6 3s^2 3p^6 4s^2 3d^1$.

Now Figure 3.2 shows that the capacity of a d shell is 10 electrons, so after calcium there is a sequence of 10 elements during which the 3d shell is filled up. These are the elements from scandium (atomic number 21) to zinc (atomic number 30) inclusive, which are members of the transition element block. In Figure 3.8, which shows how the build-up of electron configuration leads to the full Periodic Table, such transition elements are coloured mauve.

When the 3d sub-shell is full at zinc, then the filling of a new sub-shell can begin.

○ What sub-shell is this?

○ Figure 3.7 shows that it is 4p.

As Figure 3.2 shows, p sub-shells have a capacity of six electrons. Thus after zinc, there is a sequence of six elements, from gallium (atomic number 31) to krypton (atomic number 36) inclusive, in which the 4p sub-shell is filled up. As Figure 3.8 shows, these complete the fourth period of the table. The reason why the fourth period, which contains 18 elements, is so much longer than the third, which contains eight, is the presence of 10 transition elements spanning the region in which the 3d sub-shell is filled up.

Figure 3.8, then, shows how this procedure leads to a periodicity in outer electron configuration that matches the periodicity in chemical properties expressed by Figure 12.6 of Block 6. The essential point is that elements in the same column usually have

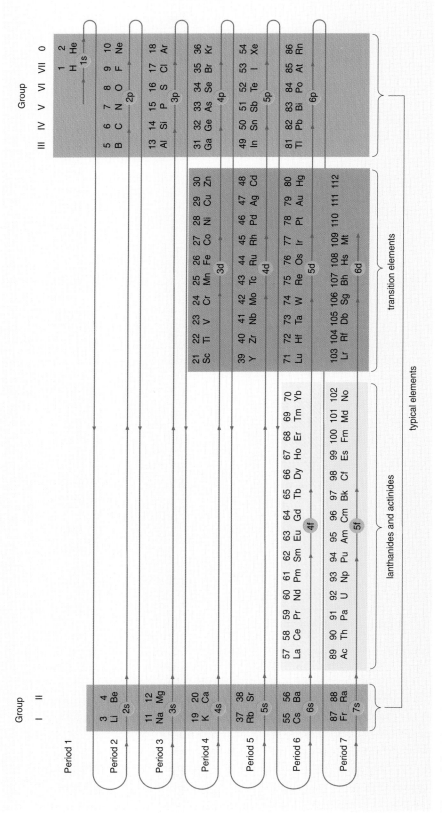

Figure 3.8 The winding arrowed pathway shows how the order of sub-shell energy and filling (Figures 3.6 and 3.7) generates the full Periodic Table. Similar elements in the same column usually have similar outer electron configurations.

similar outer electron configurations. The four rows of 10 transition elements in Figure 3.8 span regions in which d sub-shells are filling. The twin rows of 14 elements called lanthanides, and 14 elements called actinides, cover regions in which f sub-shells are filled. Remember that, as Figure 3.2 shows, the capacity of an f sub-shell is 14 electrons.

In Block 6 Activity 12.1, you were told that the transition elements are all metals and form many coloured compounds. The 14 lanthanides and 14 actinides resemble one another even more closely than this. They too are all metals, and for all 14 lanthanides, and for eight of the 14 actinides, the most prominent valency is three.

Finally, we have the typical elements which, as you saw in Block 6 Activity 12.1, occur at the extremes of the Periodic Table, coloured green in Figure 3.8. The two columns to the left, Groups I and II, span regions in which s shells are filled; the six columns to the right — Groups III–VII and Group 0 — span regions in which p sub-shells are filled. These make up the mini Periodic Table used so extensively in the CD-ROM activity of Block 6.

3.4 The mini Periodic Table for the typical elements

In Block 6, we stripped Figure 3.8 down to a mini Periodic Table by removing the central blocks of the transition elements, the lanthanides and actinides, and then pushing the two separated blocks of the typical elements together. The result is shown in Figure 3.9.

Figure 3.9 A mini Periodic Table for the typical elements; it consists of eight columns or groups, and seven rows or periods. Along the top are the group numbers in roman numerals, and the outer electron configurations of the atoms of each group.

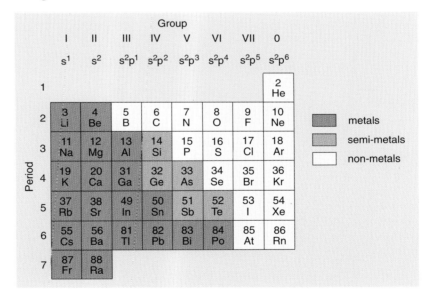

First, notice that, for the reasons given in Section 3.2.1, we have left hydrogen out. Now let's consider the electron structures. So far, we have spoken of similarities in outer electron configurations, but, for any particular atom, we have not made a clear distinction between the outer electrons and the rest. For the *typical elements* this is easy to do. The outer electrons are simply the electrons in the outer shell of the atom, that is, the electrons in the occupied sub-shells of highest principal quantum number.

Let us compare oxygen and sulfur, which both occur in Group VI. In Activity 3.1, you worked out their electron configurations. Refer back to this now.

○ Write down the occupied sub-shells of highest principal quantum number for both elements. In each case, what is the total number of electrons in the outer shell?

○ For oxygen, the occupied sub-shells of highest principal quantum number are 2s and 2p, with the occupancies $2s^2$ and $2p^4$. Those of the sulfur atom are 3s and 3p, with the occupancies $3s^2$ and $3p^4$. In both cases, there is a total of six electrons in the outer shell.

With the exception of helium, the number of outer electrons of any atom in Figure 3.9 is easily obtained from the configurations given at the top of each group. These show that the typical elements have outer electron configurations either of the type ns^x, where $x = 1$ or 2, or of the type $ns^2 np^x$, where x runs from 1 to 6. For any particular element, n is the principal quantum number of the outer occupied shell. This can easily be found from Figure 3.9, because it is equal to the number of the period in which the element is to be found. The outer electrons are simply those in occupied sub-shells with this principal quantum number. Thus, according to Figure 3.9, oxygen and sulfur have outer electron configurations of the type $ns^2 np^4$. As oxygen is in the second period of Figure 3.9, $n = 2$; as sulfur is in the third, $n = 3$. In both cases, as you saw earlier, the number of outer electrons is six.

So our mini Periodic Table confirms the main conclusion of Sections 1–3: atoms in the same group of the Periodic Table usually have similar outer electron configurations. It also shows that, for the typical elements, the total number of outer electrons is usually equal to the group number. Thus oxygen and sulfur, which occur in Group VI, have six outer electrons. The exceptions are the noble gases of Group 0: in Figure 3.9, neon for example has eight outer electrons ($2s^2 2p^6$). Even here, however, there is a weasel-like way out! In neon, the 2s and 2p sub-shells are full, and the sub-shell of next highest energy is 3s. One might argue that neon's outer shell has principal quantum number 3, and contains zero electrons. Then the number of outer electrons of *all* of the atoms in Figure 3.9 would be equal to the group number!

3.5 Summary of Sections 1–3

1 Electrons in atoms are arranged in a series of shells numbered 1, 2, 3, 4 ... etc., this number being the principal quantum number, n. Electrons in shells of higher principal quantum number are more likely to be farther from the nucleus than those in shells of lower principal quantum number.

2 The shells of electrons can be divided into sub-shells. The number of sub-shells in any shell is equal to the shell's principal quantum number.

3 The first sub-shell in any shell is denoted s. If there is a second, it is denoted p, if a third, d, and if a fourth, f. Thus the possible sub-shells for the shell with $n = 4$ are 4s, 4p, 4d and 4f. The maximum numbers of electrons that s, p, d and f sub-shells can contain are 2, 6, 10 and 14, respectively.

4 To find the electron configuration of an atom, write down the sub-shells in order of increasing energy, and add the electrons to them, starting with the sub-shell of lowest energy. When a sub-shell has been filled, move on to the sub-shell of next higher energy. Indicate the number of electrons in each occupied sub-shell by a superscript after the sub-shell symbol.

5   It transpires that the groups of similar elements that appear in columns in the Periodic Table usually have atoms with similar outer electron configurations. This explains chemical periodicity.

6   For the typical elements, the outer electrons are those in the sub-shells of highest principal quantum number. The typical elements in Groups I and II have outer electron configurations of the type ns^1 and ns^2, respectively, where n is the period number. The typical elements in Groups III–VII and 0 have outer electron configurations of the type $ns^2 np^x$ where x runs from 1 to 6. The group numbers are equal to the numbers of outer electrons.

You have now worked out how the electron configurations of atoms change with atomic number, and shown how this explains the shape of the Periodic Table. This operation was first carried out by Niels Bohr (Block 7, Figure 3.4), and it won him the 1922 Nobel Prize for Physics. He called the process one in which 'the neutral atom is built up by the capture and binding of electrons to the nucleus one by one'. Our task was easier than Bohr's because we knew the quantum rules and the order of sub-shell energy levels. Bohr had to guess both these things from the form of the Periodic Table, and other bits of evidence. Nevertheless, Section 3 should have helped you to appreciate one of the great moments of science: the moment that explained chemical periodicity and established the electron configurations of atoms.

Question 3.2   What is the principal quantum number of the 5f, 4d and 3p sub-shells? What is the *maximum* number of electrons that each of these sub-shells can hold? ◄

Question 3.3   Which of the following sub-shells exist, and which do not: 5d, 1p, 3f, 6s, 4p and 2d? Explain your answer. ◄

Question 3.4   Use Figure 3.3 to work out the electron configurations of the carbon and silicon atoms, which have atomic numbers 6 and 14, respectively. Carbon and silicon are typical elements and occur in the same group of the Periodic Table. Show how your electron configurations are consistent with this. Are the numbers of outer electrons in carbon and silicon equal to the group number? ◄

Question 3.5   Use the period numbers and types of electron configuration in Figure 3.9 to write down the outer electron configurations of tellurium (atomic number 52) and thallium (atomic number 81). Are their numbers of outer electrons equal to their group numbers? ◄

Activity 3.2   Working out electron configurations at high atomic number

This activity checks that you can use Figures 3.6 and 3.7 to work out full electron configurations for elements beyond calcium. ◄

Activity 3.3   Electron configurations and chemical periodicity

This CD-ROM activity revises Sections 2 and 3. But it does so by following a different path, and by providing additional self-assessment and revision questions. ◄

Chemical bonding: ionic compounds and molecular substances

4

Electron configurations can also be used to understand **chemical bonding**, the forces that hold or *bond* atoms together in chemical substances. Two very important, but very different classes of chemical substances provide the simplest demonstration of this. They are called *ionic compounds* and *molecular substances*. So you must first become acquainted with these two types. We begin with ionic compounds, which include the salts of metallic elements, such as sodium chloride and calcium chloride, that you met in Block 6.

4.1   Ionic compounds

Calcium chloride, $CaCl_2$, has a lot in common with common salt or sodium chloride, $NaCl$. Both compounds are a combination of a metallic element from the left of the Periodic Table with non-metallic chlorine, which lies to the right (see Figure 3.9). Both are solids that melt at over 750 °C.

Block 6 Section 13.3 showed that $CaCl_2$ and $NaCl$ dissolve easily in water, greatly increasing the water's conductivity. This was explained by the formation of aqueous ions. $NaCl$ dissolves to give the aqueous ions $Na^+(aq)$ and $Cl^-(aq)$. The equation is:

$$NaCl(s) \longrightarrow Na^+(aq) + Cl^-(aq) \tag{4.1}$$

What is the equation for the dissolution of solid $CaCl_2$ in water?

$$CaCl_2(s) \longrightarrow Ca^{2+}(aq) + 2Cl^-(aq) \tag{4.2}$$

As with $NaCl$, $Cl^-(aq)$ ions are formed. As the formula unit $CaCl_2$ yields two $Cl^-(aq)$ ions, the single calcium ion must carry a charge of 2+, because then the total charge is the same (zero) on each side of the equation, and the equation is correctly balanced.

So, when dissolved in liquid water, sodium chloride and calcium chloride are good conductors of electricity. But the two chlorides also turn liquid when we melt them. How good an electrical conductor is pure liquid $NaCl$ or $CaCl_2$? The answer is, very good. Figure 4.1 shows the test used in Block 6 to assess the conductivity of a liquid. Here it is applied to molten sodium chloride.

The conductivity and electrical decomposition of molten sodium chloride can be explained by assuming that the melt, like aqueous sodium chloride, contains Na^+ and Cl^- ions. Imagine two Na^+ ions drawn to the oppositely charged, negative electrode to the left of Figure 4.1. Each picks up an incoming electron and is converted into a sodium atom in molten sodium metal:

$$2Na^+(melt) + 2e^- \longrightarrow 2Na(l) \tag{4.3}$$

At the same time, two Cl^- ions migrate to the positive electrode on the right. They each deposit an electron and become chlorine atoms, which pair up to form a molecule of chlorine gas, Cl_2:

$$2Cl^-(melt) \longrightarrow Cl_2(g) + 2e^- \tag{4.4}$$

Figure 4.1 Testing the electrical conductivity of molten sodium chloride. The bulb lights up because the conductivity is high. Chlorine gas streams off the electrode wired to the positive terminal of the battery, and molten sodium metal collects around the electrode connected to the negative terminal.

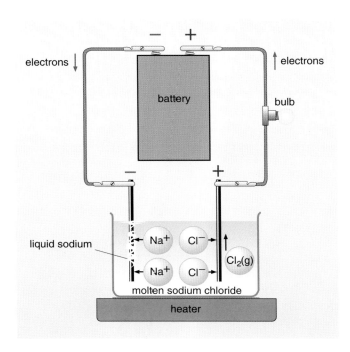

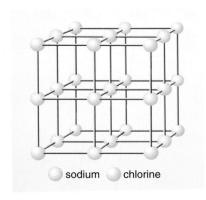

Figure 4.2

Figure 4.2 A part of the structure of sodium chloride as revealed by X-ray crystallography. Each side of the cube is about 560 pm. (The lines in the diagram are simply to help visualize the structure; they do *not* represent bonds.)

The net result is that two sodium ions and two chloride ions have been removed from the melt, and converted into sodium metal and chlorine gas. At the same time, two electrons have been removed from the negative electrode, and two electrons have been planted on the positive electrode: in effect, two electrons have jumped the gap in the molten sodium chloride between the electrodes.

So in both the liquid state, and in aqueous solution, sodium chloride consists of ions. How about in the solid state? There are well-established techniques for finding the positions of atoms in solids. The best-known is called X-ray crystallography, and Figure 4.2 shows you what it reveals about sodium chloride. Each grain of table salt that you use every day is made up of about 10^{18} tiny cubes like this. Look first at the sodium at the centre of the cube in Figure 4.2.

● What type of atom is closest to this sodium, and how many of them are there?

○ The sodium is surrounded by six chlorines at the centres of the cube faces.

How about the atoms around chlorine? To see these clearly, you must look beyond the cube of Figure 4.2. The crystalline fragments in your salt-cellar are built up from these little cubes, joined through their faces. Thus a cube deep within the crystal is joined through its six faces to six others, which completely surround it. Figure 4.3 uses just two such cubes to show you what we mean by 'joined'. The identical adjoining faces of the two cubes *merge into one*. Now look at the chlorine at the centre of Figure 4.3.

● What type of atom is closest to this chlorine, and how many of them are there?

○ The chlorine is surrounded by six sodiums in just the way that sodium is surrounded by chlorine in Figure 4.2.

We can explain this type of structure by supposing that what we have called the sodium atom in Figure 4.2 is present as the ion Na$^+$, and the chlorine as the ion Cl$^-$.

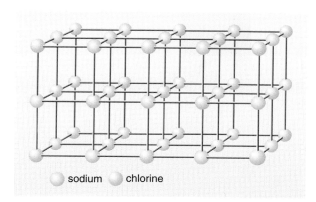

Figure 4.3 How two of the units in Figure 4.2 are joined through a cube face in solid sodium chloride.

sodium   chlorine

In Blocks 5 and 6, you saw that unlike charges attract each other, so each ion will attract, and surround itself by, as many ions of opposite charge as possible. This results in the arrangement of lowest energy. This ionic picture of the structure is shown in Figure 4.4. It can explain the conductivity of molten NaCl: the ions exist in the solid, and are still there after it has been melted. The picture also accounts for the high melting temperature. The oppositely charged ions are held together by strong attractive forces, so a large amount of energy is needed to tear them apart and melt the structure down.

If sodium chloride dissolves in a solvent, its ions must separate and drift off into the solution. As the attractive forces between the ions are strong, that should not usually happen. This is true; sodium chloride does not, for example, dissolve in grease-removing solvents, such as petrol or dry-cleaning fluids. The striking exception, of course, is water, in which it dissolves readily. What is special about water is discussed in Section 7.

Substances that fit this type of picture, such as calcium chloride and sodium chloride, are called **ionic compounds**. A typical ionic compound is a solid at room temperature, has high melting and boiling temperatures, and conducts electricity in the molten state. It barely dissolves in petrol, but it may dissolve easily in water, and if this happens, the aqueous solution is a good electrical conductor. The structure of the solid is one in which each ion surrounds itself with other ions of opposite charge. Many compounds fit this picture. Among them are the salts that you met in Block 6; in particular, the alkali metal halides, MX, where M is an alkali metal (Li, Na, K, Rb, or Cs), and X is a halogen (F, Cl, Br or I). These solids are assemblies of the singly-charged ions M^+ and X^-, mostly arranged as in Figure 4.4. The Group II metals magnesium and calcium form ionic halides, MX_2, containing the ions M^{2+} and X^-.

Figure 4.2 reinforces the distinction between empirical and molecular formulae that we made in Block 6. The formula NaCl for sodium chloride is an empirical formula: it merely tells us that, in sodium chloride, there are equal numbers of sodiums and chlorines. This condition is automatically fulfilled when many cubes of the Figure 4.2 type are joined through their faces. But Figure 4.2 provides no grounds for saying that NaCl is the *molecular formula* of sodium chloride. Indeed, quite the opposite; the six chlorines around the sodium in Figure 4.2 all lie the *same distance* away. There are no grounds for singling out just one of them and coupling it with the sodium to form an NaCl molecule. The structure provides no evidence for the existence of discrete NaCl molecules; NaCl is a *non-molecular* compound.

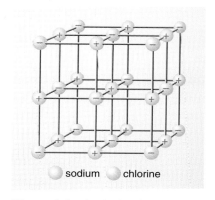

sodium   chlorine

Figure 4.4 An ionic picture of solid sodium chloride, which explains important properties of the substance. The solid is regarded as an assembly of Na^+ and Cl^- ions.

4.2 Molecular substances

In **molecular substances**, discrete molecules can be picked out. In this and other respects, they are very different from ionic compounds. For a start, they have much lower melting and boiling temperatures. Thus many of them are known to you as gases: hydrogen (H_2), oxygen (O_2), nitrogen (N_2), hydrogen chloride (HCl), chlorine (Cl_2), methane (CH_4), ammonia (NH_3) and carbon dioxide (CO_2). Then there are some, such as water (H_2O) and nitrogen trichloride (NCl_3), that are liquids at room temperature. The halogen elements are good examples of molecular substances. Fluorine (F_2) and chlorine (Cl_2) are yellowish gases. Although bromine (Br_2) is a red liquid and iodine a deep purple solid, bromine has a boiling temperature of only 60 °C, and iodine melts at only 114 °C and boils at 185 °C.

Another contrast with ionic compounds is the electrical conductivity in the liquid state. Liquid bromine, liquid water and liquid iodine are all poor conductors. This is also true of the gases that we have mentioned when they are liquefied by cooling. Molecular substances are poor conductors of electricity in the liquid state. Another of their characteristics is that they often dissolve in petrol or dry-cleaning fluid. Bromine and iodine are both soluble in these liquids.

For gases, Block 6 provided you with evidence of the existence and chemical formulae of the molecules that give molecular substances their name. But what about other states of matter? What evidence is there, for example, for the presence of molecules in *solid* molecular substances? The structure of solid iodine is shown in Figure 4.5. It contains pairs of iodine atoms separated by a distance of 268 pm. By contrast, the shortest distance between different pairs is considerably longer (356 pm). This is evidence that solid iodine contains I_2 molecules. Now, the binding forces between atoms are essentially electrical, and arise from the forces between the charged electrons. Electrical forces are stronger at shorter distances, so the short distance between the atoms within a pair — the atoms in an I_2 molecule — suggests that the forces holding these atoms together are strong. By contrast, the longer distance between different pairs (molecules) tells us that the forces that hold one I_2 molecule to another are weaker.

Figure 4.5 What X-ray crystallography reveals about solid iodine. If iodine atoms that are separated by a short distance (AB) of 268 pm are connected by bonds, the structure becomes a collection of *pairs* of iodine atoms. These pairs are I_2 molecules, which are separated from one another by a longer distance of at least 356 pm (BC).

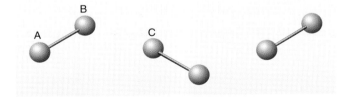

Why does iodine have low melting and boiling temperatures?

In solid iodine, different I_2 molecules are held together by weak forces, so only a little energy needs to be transferred to them by heating to separate them and create first a liquid, and then a gas. Both the liquid and the gas also contain I_2 molecules. To melt and then boil iodine it is not necessary to take the I_2 molecules themselves apart.

This also explains why liquid iodine does not conduct electricity: the liquid contains not ions but I_2 molecules. The ease with which the iodine molecules can be separated also explains the solubility of iodine in a solvent like petrol. The solid crystal falls apart, and individual I_2 molecules drift off into solution.

Finally, what about the distinction between empirical and molecular formulae? Iodine contains only iodine atoms, so if we wrote an *empirical formula* for solid iodine, it would be I(s). But Figure 4.5 gives us additional information: there are grounds for thinking that the iodine atoms are grouped in pairs as I_2 molecules. We can act on this by writing a molecular formula for solid iodine, which is I_2(s), something that we could not do for sodium chloride. Solid iodine is a *molecular* substance.

4.2.1 Molecular substances and valency

Molecular substances contain not ions but molecules, e.g. H_2, O_2, N_2, F_2, Cl_2, HCl, CH_4, CO_2, NH_3, Br_2, H_2O, NCl_3, CCl_4 and I_2. In Block 6 Section 10.7, these formulae were explained by assigning a fixed valency to the atoms of carbon, nitrogen, oxygen, hydrogen and the halogens.

⬤ What valencies did we assign to each of these atoms?

◯ One to hydrogen and the halogens, two to oxygen, three to nitrogen and four to carbon.

In Block 6, valency was just a number that could be used to predict the formulae of compounds. However, when dealing with molecular substances, it can tell us more. In particular, it can tell us how the atoms are linked together in the molecule. This information is obtained from a two-dimensional drawing called the **structural formula** of the molecule. Consider, for example, the molecules H_2, Cl_2, NH_3 and NCl_3. Their structural formulae are shown here as structures **4.1**–**4.4**. In these diagrams, the lines represent the bonds between atoms. (In this course, we adopt the convention of referring to structural formulae either by name or by a number in bold type, such as **4.1**.)

$$H-H \qquad Cl-Cl \qquad \begin{matrix} H-N-H \\ | \\ H \end{matrix} \qquad \begin{matrix} Cl-N-Cl \\ | \\ Cl \end{matrix}$$

$$\textbf{4.1} \qquad\qquad \textbf{4.2} \qquad\qquad \textbf{4.3} \qquad\qquad \textbf{4.4}$$

Structural formulae are put together as follows. First, they must have the same molecular formula as the molecule. Thus structure **4.3** contains one nitrogen and three hydrogen atoms, as does the molecular formula of ammonia, NH_3. Secondly, those atoms are then connected so that the number of bonds emerging from any atom is equal to its valency. Thus in structure **4.3**, three bonds emerge from the nitrogen atom, and one from each hydrogen atom.

Question 4.1   Draw structural formulae for molecules of the compounds hydrogen chloride (HCl), methane (CH_4), carbon tetrachloride (CCl_4) and water (H_2O) in this way. ◀

Notice how the example of water in Question 4.1 emphasizes that structural formulae tell us nothing about the three-dimensional shape of the molecule. They just show the valencies of atoms, and *what other atoms any atom in the molecule is connected to*. Both the straight and the bent structural formula for water do this, so either is satisfactory.

The atoms in the structural formulae that you have seen so far have been linked by single lines or **single bonds**. But this is not always the case. Consider O_2 and CO_2. If oxygen and carbon are to have their familiar valencies of two and four respectively, each pair of atoms must be connected by two lines and not one, as in structures **4.5** and **4.6**. In these examples, the atoms are said to be bound together by **double bonds**.

$$O=O \qquad O=C=O$$
$$\textbf{4.5} \qquad\quad \textbf{4.6}$$

○ Draw a structural formula of the molecule N_2 in which nitrogen has its common valency of three.

○ Here the two atoms are linked by *three* lines: a **triple bond**, as in structure **4.7**.

$N \equiv N$

4.7

In Section 5, you will find out more about the nature of these bonds, and why the carbon, nitrogen, oxygen, halogen and hydrogen atoms have the valencies that they do.

4.3 Ionic compounds, molecular substances and the Periodic Table

The substances in Sections 4–4.2 contained 15 chemical elements in all, and Figure 4.6 shows where those elements (apart from hydrogen) lie in the mini Periodic Table of Figure 3.9. Our molecular substances contained only non-metallic elements, which lie at the right-hand end of the table. By contrast, the ionic compounds were all a combination of a metallic element on the left of the table, with a non-metallic element to the right. Notice also that, in the ionic compounds, it is the metallic elements that form the positive ions (e.g. Li^+, Na^+, K^+, Mg^{2+} and Ca^{2+}), and the non-metallic elements that are present as negative ions (e.g. F^-, Cl^-, Br^- and I^-). These patterns will help us, in the next section, to explain the chemical formulae of the compounds, and the forces that hold them together.

Figure 4.6 Elements from which our examples of ionic compounds and molecular substances were formed, and their places in the Periodic Table.

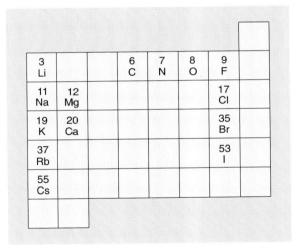

Activity 4.1 Viewing the properties of ionic compounds and molecular substances

In this activity, you will see the differences between ionic compounds and molecular substances on video. ◀

4.4 Summary of Section 4

1 Many important chemical substances can be classified as either ionic or molecular.

2 A typical ionic compound is a solid with a high melting temperature, which conducts electricity when molten, and does not dissolve appreciably in solvents like petrol or dry-cleaning fluids. It may, however, dissolve readily in water, and

if it does, its aqueous solution will be a conductor. It can be pictured as a structure in which each ion surrounds itself with ions of opposite charge, and in which discrete molecules with the empirical formula of the solid cannot be picked out.

3   A typical molecular substance has low melting and boiling temperatures, and a structure in which discrete molecules can be picked out. It often dissolves readily in solvents like petrol or dry-cleaning fluids, but these solutions, like the molten substance, do not conduct electricity.

4   The molecules in many molecular substances can be represented by a structural formula in which every atom is connected to others by a number of lines or bonds equal to its valency.

Question 4.2   When lithium metal is heated in hydrogen gas, white solid lithium hydride, LiH, is formed. Its crystal structure is shown in Figure 4.7.

(a) Explain why this is consistent with the classification of lithium hydride as an ionic compound.

(b) Alkali metals, such as lithium and sodium, form ions with a single positive charge. If lithium is present as Li^+, what other ion does the compound contain?

(c) When lithium hydride is heated, it melts at 680 °C, and the liquid is a good conductor of electricity. If the conductivity is tested with the equipment shown in Figure 4.1, a gas streams off the positive electrode, and a molten metal collects around the negative electrode. Identify the gas and the metal, and write equations for the processes occurring at each electrode. ◄

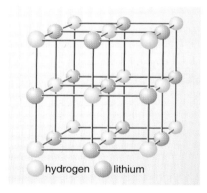

hydrogen   lithium

Figure 4.7   Part of the crystal structure of lithium hydride, LiH.

Question 4.3   On a cold day, hydrogen fluoride, HF, is an intensely corrosive liquid, but its boiling temperature is only 20 °C. It dissolves in petrol, although only slightly, and freezes to a solid at –83 °C. The crystal structure of the solid shows that it contains zig-zag chains consisting of hydrogen and fluorine atoms. One of these chains is pictured in Figure 4.8.

(a) Would you classify hydrogen fluoride as an ionic compound, or a molecular substance?

(b) Would you expect liquid hydrogen fluoride to be a good conductor of electricity?

Explain your answers. ◄

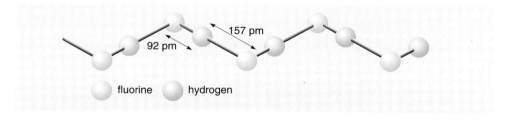

157 pm

92 pm

fluorine   hydrogen

Figure 4.8   The distances between the atoms in the zig-zag chains found in solid hydrogen fluoride.

Question 4.4   In the following list of elements, the most common valencies are given in brackets: carbon (4), oxygen (2), sulfur (2), fluorine (1) and chlorine (1). The following substances contain molecules with the molecular formulae given in brackets: oxygen (O_2), dichlorine monoxide (Cl_2O), carbon tetrafluoride (CF_4), carbon disulfide (CS_2), and the poisonous gas, phosgene ($COCl_2$). Draw structural formulae for each molecule that are consistent with these valencies. ◄

5 Explaining chemistry through electron structure

The big scientific idea that underlies our explanation of the Periodic Table in Section 3.2 is as follows: *chemistry can be explained in terms of the electron structures of atoms*. What follows is a more detailed example of this idea.

5.1 Simplified electron structures

Our example requires the electron structures of the first 20 elements. Up till now, electron structures of atoms have been given as the electron configurations in columns 2, 5 and 8 of Table 5.1. Here we can make do with a simpler form. This new form shows the electron content of successive *shells*, rather than of successive sub-shells. For example, the electron configuration of the silicon atom is $1s^2 2s^2 2p^6 3s^2 3p^2$; it contains sub-shells from shells with the principal quantum numbers 1, 2 and 3.

⬤ How many electrons are there in each of these three shells?

◯ There are two electrons in the 1s sub-shell, eight in the 2s and 2p sub-shells, and four in the 3s and 3p sub-shells.

An alternative way of writing the electron structure of the silicon atom is therefore (2,8,4), where the numbers separated by commas show the electron content of successive shells. In Table 5.1, this **shell structure** of the atom is tabulated for the first 20 elements.

Table 5.1 Electron configurations and shell structures for the first 20 elements.

Atom	Electron configuration	Shell structure	Atom	Electron configuration	Shell structure	Atom	Electron configuration	Shell structure
H	$1s^1$	(1)						
He	$1s^2$	(2)						
Li	$1s^2 2s^1$	(2,1)	Na	$1s^2 2s^2 2p^6 3s^1$	(2,8,1)	K	$1s^2 2s^2 2p^6 3s^2 3p^6 4s^1$	(2,8,8,1)
Be	$1s^2 2s^2$	(2,2)	Mg	$1s^2 2s^2 2p^6 3s^2$	(2,8,2)	Ca	$1s^2 2s^2 2p^6 3s^2 3p^6 4s^2$	(2,8,8,2)
B	$1s^2 2s^2 2p^1$	(2,3)	Al	$1s^2 2s^2 2p^6 3s^2 3p^1$	(2,8,3)			
C	$1s^2 2s^2 2p^2$	(2,4)	Si	$1s^2 2s^2 2p^6 3s^2 3p^2$	(2,8,4)			
N	$1s^2 2s^2 2p^3$	(2,5)	P	$1s^2 2s^2 2p^6 3s^2 3p^3$	(2,8,5)			
O	$1s^2 2s^2 2p^4$	(2,6)	S	$1s^2 2s^2 2p^6 3s^2 3p^4$	(2,8,6)			
F	$1s^2 2s^2 2p^5$	(2,7)	Cl	$1s^2 2s^2 2p^6 3s^2 3p^5$	(2,8,7)			
Ne	$1s^2 2s^2 2p^6$	(2,8)	Ar	$1s^2 2s^2 2p^6 3s^2 3p^6$	(2,8,8)			

These shell structures can be used to tackle an important problem. When two elements react to form a compound, their atoms tend to combine in a particular ratio. For example, lithium and hydrogen yield LiH, not Li_2H or LiH_2. Likewise, hydrogen and oxygen gases react together to form H_2O, not OH or HO_2. Why is there this strong preference for the combinations LiH and H_2O? This kind of question can, in part, be answered by two simple theories of chemical bonding. One theory answers for ionic compounds, and the other for molecular substances. But in both theories the noble gas atoms and their electron structures play a very important part. So first, we revisit noble gas chemistry.

5.2 The noble gases revisited

You met the noble gases in Section 12.1 of Block 6. They all form chemical compounds with reluctance. Indeed, the three noble gases with which we shall be most concerned, helium, neon and argon, form no chemical compounds whatsoever. Then again, the molecules of which the noble gases are composed consist of single atoms.

○ Why is this also a sign that the noble gases are reluctant to enter into chemical combination?

○ Unlike, say, hydrogen (H_2) or nitrogen (N_2), one noble gas atom is unwilling to combine with another of the same sort to form gas molecules containing more than one atom.

Now, when atoms combine, the arrangement of their electrons is disturbed. The electron structures of the noble gases must therefore be remarkably stable to disturbance. This is the essential idea underlying the simplest theories of chemical bonding.

> The electron structures of noble gas atoms are especially stable, and many elements try to attain these structures when they react to form chemical compounds.

According to this assumption, the noble gases are chemically inert because they already have noble gas electron structures. Three examples of these structures appear in Table 5.2. But how can one element attain the electron structure of another? According to the simplest theories, there are two ways. The first leads to ionic compounds and involves *electron transfer*; we shall deal with this first.

5.3 Ionic bonding

As Question 4.2 showed, lithium hydride, LiH, is an assembly of Li^+ and H^- ions. But why do the ions have the charges that they do; why, for example, is the lithium ion Li^+ and not Li^- or Li^{2+}? Let's look at the shell structures. For the hydrogen, helium and lithium atoms, these are (1), (2) and (2,1), respectively. Now, the lithium atom can form an Li^+ ion by losing an electron:

$$Li \longrightarrow Li^+ + e^- \tag{5.1}$$

Table 5.2 The shell structures of helium, neon and argon atoms.

He	(2)
Ne	(2,8)
Ar	(2,8,8)

The easiest electron to lose is the solitary electron in the outer shell, because this is farthest from the nucleus.

● What is the shell structure of the Li$^+$ ion. To what atom does this structure correspond?

○ Removal of the outer electron from (2,1) leaves us with (2). This is the shell structure of the helium atom.

Now suppose that we take the electron that we removed from the lithium atom and add it to a hydrogen atom to form an H$^-$ ion:

$$H + e^- \longrightarrow H^- \tag{5.2}$$

● What is the shell structure of the H$^-$ ion. To what atom does its structure correspond?

○ Addition of an electron to the hydrogen atom shell structure, (1), gives us (2); the hydride ion, H$^-$, has the shell structure of the helium atom.

This is why lithium and hydrogen react to form the ionic compound LiH. The atoms try, by a reaction, to attain noble gas configurations, which are especially stable. If every lithium atom loses an electron, which is then transferred to a hydrogen atom, the result will be equal numbers of Li$^+$ and H$^-$ ions, each of which has the electron configuration of helium. Because the two kinds of ion have equal and opposite charges, equal numbers of them can arrange themselves as in Figure 4.7 to form the neutral, ionic compound with empirical formula LiH.

Notice that although H$^-$, He and Li$^+$ all have the same electron structure, they are still very different. This is because they have different numbers of protons in the nucleus (Figure 5.1).

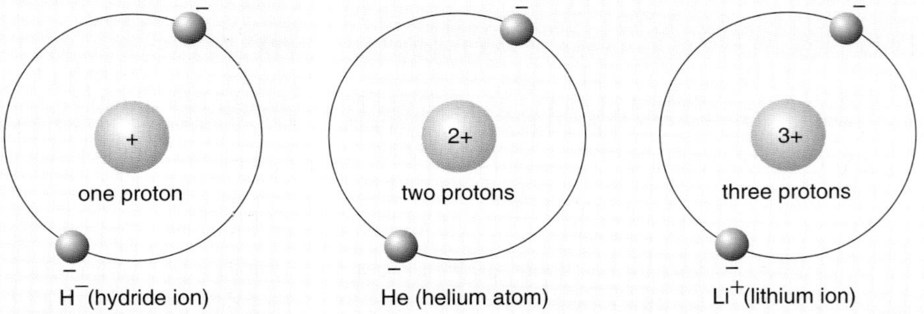

Figure 5.1   The numbers of protons and electrons in the hydride ion, the helium atom and the lithium ion. All have the same electron structure with two electrons, but there are different numbers of protons in the nucleus. The helium atom is neutral with equal numbers of protons and electrons; in the hydride ion, the electrons exceed the protons by one, so the ion carries a single negative charge; in the lithium ion, the protons exceed the electrons by one, so the ion carries a single positive charge.

This explanation can be applied to all the alkali metal halides and hydrides that have formulae of the type MX. The Group I alkali metal atoms have the electron structure of a noble gas *plus* one extra outer electron; the Group VII elements, the halogens, and hydrogen have the electron structure of a noble gas atom *minus* one outer electron. If every M atom transfers its additional outer electron to an X atom, equal numbers of M$^+$ and X$^-$ ions with the electron structures of noble gas atoms can then combine to give ionic compounds of empirical formula MX. In the resulting assembly of ions, M$^+$X$^-$, the compound is held together by the electrical attraction between the positive and negative ions. This is called **ionic bonding**.

Let's check that you understand this by looking at the case of sodium chloride. As Figure 5.2 shows, the sodium and chlorine atoms have the shell structures (2,8,1) and (2,8,7), respectively.

							He 2
Li 2,1	Be 2,2	B 2,3	C 2,4	N 2,5	O 2,6	F 2,7	Ne 2,8
Na 2,8,1	Mg 2,8,2	Al 2,8,3	Si 2,8,4	P 2,8,5	S 2,8,6	Cl 2,8,7	Ar 2,8,8
K 2,8,8,1	Ca 2,8,8,2						

Figure 5.2   A periodic table showing shell structures for atoms 2–20.

○ If the sodium atom transfers one of its electrons to a chlorine atom, what ions are formed, and to what noble gas atoms do the shell structures of those ions correspond?

○ When a sodium atom loses its outer electron, it becomes an Na^+ ion with the shell structure (2,8); as Figure 5.2 shows, this is the electron structure of the neon atom. When the lost electron is transferred to a chlorine atom, it enters the partly filled outer shell, and a Cl^- ion with the structure (2,8,8) is formed; this is the shell structure of the argon atom.

Because the ions with noble gas structures have equal and opposite net charges, equal numbers must be combined to give a neutral assembly Na^+Cl^-. Hence, the empirical formula of sodium chloride is NaCl.

Question 5.1   Write down the shell structure of the calcium atom. How could calcium most easily attain the electron structure of a noble gas? What therefore is the symbol of the calcium ion? What would be the empirical formula of calcium chloride? ◀

As you know, the formula $CaCl_2$ predicted in Question 5.1 is correct. Another calcium compound with which you are familiar is quicklime, CaO. This too is an ionic compound containing Ca^{2+} ions with the electron structure of argon.

○ So what will be the charge on the oxide ion?

○ The formula CaO shows that the compound contains equal numbers of calciums and oxygens; as calcium is present as Ca^{2+} and the compound is electrically neutral, the oxygen must be present as O^{2-}.

○ Does the oxide ion, O^{2-}, have a noble gas structure?

○ It does. An oxygen atom has the shell structure (2,6), and the two additional electrons go into the outer, partly filled shell to give (2,8). This is the shell structure of the neon atom.

To sum up, the Group I elements occur in their compounds as singly charged positive ions. Magnesium and calcium in Group II form compounds containing the ions Mg^{2+} and Ca^{2+}. The halogens (Group VII) and hydrogen can form compounds containing singly charged negative ions. All these ions have noble gas shell structures. Their charges are such that neutral halides of the Group I metals have empirical formulae MX. Those of the Group II metals are MX_2.

Figure 5.3 Until he was 14, Gilbert Newton Lewis (1875–1946) was educated at home in Nebraska by his parents. One of the most remarkable things about him was that he did not win a Nobel Prize, since his idea of the electron-pair bond has been called 'the most productive and important contribution that has ever been made to the subject of valency and chemical bonding'. During the First World War, he trained gas warfare specialists and was made a Lieutenant-Colonel. A love of cigars may have contributed to his death from heart failure while doing an experiment.

5.4 Covalent bonding

A molecular substance, such as chlorine gas, Cl_2, whose structural formula appears in structure **4.2**, is nothing like an ionic compound, such as NaCl. Nor can chlorine gas be represented as a collection of ions with noble gas structures. Suppose, for example, that one of the two chlorines in the Cl_2 molecule is a Cl^- ion with the electron structure of argon.

⬤ What charge and electron structure will the other chlorine have?

◯ To maintain neutrality, it must be present as Cl^+. This ion does not have a noble gas structure; it has the electron structure of the sulfur atom, the element *preceding* chlorine in the Periodic Table.

In 1916, the American chemist, G. N. Lewis (Figure 5.3) proposed a new theory which, when applied to chlorine gas, gave each chlorine atom a noble gas structure. Lewis suggested that the bonds formed between the atoms in molecules arose not from electron transfer as in ionic compounds, but from *electron sharing*. The atoms in the molecule share *pairs of electrons*, and each shared pair constitutes a **covalent bond**. Thus we can represent two chlorine atoms by structure **5.1**. Here the seven dots on one atom and the seven crosses on the other represent the seven outer electrons of the shell structure (2,8,7). Then the chlorine molecule, Cl_2, is written as in structure **5.2**.

$$: \overset{\cdot\cdot}{\underset{\cdot\cdot}{Cl}} \cdot \quad \overset{\times\times}{\underset{\times\times}{_\times Cl_\times}} \qquad : \overset{\cdot\cdot}{\underset{\cdot\cdot}{Cl}} \overset{\times\times}{\underset{\times\times}{_\times Cl_\times}}$$

$$\textbf{5.1} \qquad\qquad\qquad \textbf{5.2}$$

Structure **5.2** is called a **Lewis structure**. By convention, the outer electrons around each atom are grouped in pairs. *The pair of electrons that falls between the two chlorines is counted towards the electron structures of both.* The electron pair thus shared between the atoms is equivalent to a chemical bond.

⬤ What electron structure is thereby achieved by the two chlorines in the Cl_2 molecule?

◯ Because the shared electron pair is counted towards the shell structure of both atoms, both atoms gain access to an extra electron. In this sense, each gains one electron and attains the shell structure of argon; that is, they both have eight outer electrons (2,8,8).

Because just *one* pair of electrons is shared in the Lewis structure of Cl_2, the bond is a *single* bond. The electron pair is therefore an interpretation of the single line drawn between the two chlorine atoms in structure **4.2**.

As further examples, consider the molecules NCl_3 and H_2O. Nitrogen has five outer electrons (2,5), hydrogen has one (1), and oxygen has six (2,6). Suppose that the outer electrons on the nitrogen and oxygen atoms are represented by crosses, and those on the hydrogen and chlorine atoms by dots. Then each atom attains a noble gas structure in Lewis structures **5.3** and **5.4**.

In NCl_3, the nitrogen gains one electron from each of the three electron pairs that it shares with the three chlorine atoms. It thus achieves the electron structure of neon (2,8). Notice that the three shared electron pairs needed to give nitrogen this structure explain why the valency of nitrogen is three in structure **4.4**. The neon structure is also attained by oxygen in the water molecule. Each hydrogen gains one electron from the single electron-pair bond that it forms with oxygen, and attains the electron structure of helium, (2).

$$: \overset{\cdot\cdot}{\underset{\cdot\cdot}{Cl}} \overset{\times\times}{\underset{\times}{_\times N}} \overset{\cdot\cdot}{\underset{\cdot\cdot}{Cl}} : \qquad H \overset{\times\times}{\underset{\times\cdot}{_\times O_\times}}$$
$$: \overset{}{\underset{\cdot\cdot}{Cl}} : \qquad\qquad H$$
$$\textbf{5.3} \qquad\qquad\qquad \textbf{5.4}$$

○ Now draw a Lewis structure for the methane molecule, CH_4.

○ Carbon has four outer electrons (2,4). It can attain the electron structure of neon (2,8), by gaining four electrons from four electron pairs. Each hydrogen again attains the helium structure. The Lewis structure for methane is thus **5.5**.

So far, any two atoms in our Lewis structures have been held together by just one electron-pair bond. But sometimes two or even three shared pairs may be involved. The Lewis structures and structural formulae for CO_2 and N_2 are shown in Figure 5.4.

The *two* electron *pairs* between each oxygen and the central carbon are an interpretation of each carbon–oxygen *double* bond. As the examples of CO_2 and CH_4 show, carbon has a valency of four because, when it exercises that valency, it attains the electron structure of neon. Likewise, the *three* shared *pairs* in the N_2 molecule are equivalent to a *triple* bond.

So the Lewis structures of structures **5.2–5.5** and Figure 5.4 tell us why hydrogen, carbon, nitrogen, oxygen and chlorine have the valencies that they do. That valency is the number of shared electron-pair bonds that the atom must form if it is to attain the electron structure of a noble gas. Thus hydrogen and oxygen form water, H_2O, rather than HO or HO_2, because this molecular formula enables both elements to attain the electron structure of a noble gas.

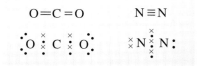

5.5

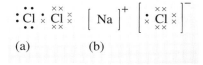

Figure 5.4 Lewis structures (bottom) and structural formulae (top) for CO_2 and N_2. All atoms have eight outer electrons.

5.5   Electronegativity

Despite their great differences, the ionic compound NaCl and the covalently bound molecular substance Cl_2 have something important in common. Figure 5.5a shows the Lewis structure of the Cl_2 molecule; Figure 5.5b represents the ions in NaCl in the same spirit. The sodium ion is shown with no outer electrons because the single outer electron of the sodium atom has become part of the chloride ion, where it is represented as a dot. Following the convention of Section 5.4, the outer electrons are grouped in pairs. In both cases, bonding involves the formation of a new electron pair in the outer electron structure of each chlorine. However, in Cl_2, because the two atoms are identical, the electron pair must be equally shared between them; in the words of Section 2, the electrons in the pair spend equal times on each atom. In NaCl, by contrast, the electron pair spends its time almost entirely on the chloride ion. From this standpoint, ionic and covalent bonding both involve the formation of electron pairs: *the difference between them lies only in the extent to which those electron pairs are shared between the two atoms.*

This link between ionic and covalent bonding is clarified by the concept of **electronegativity**. The electronegativity of an element is the power of its atom to attract electrons to itself *when forming chemical bonds*. In the Cl_2 molecule, the two identical atoms have an equal appetite for electrons: their electronegativities are equal, so the electron pair is shared equally between them. Now consider sodium chloride.

○ Which atom is the more electronegative, sodium or chlorine?

○ In sodium chloride, the electron pair has been completely taken over by chlorine, which forms a chloride ion. Imagine the sodium and chlorine atoms competing for electrons; the chlorine atoms win, so chlorine is the more electronegative.

Figure 5.5 The conventions used to draw the Lewis structure of Cl_2 (a), are here used to represent the ions in sodium chloride, (b).

So chlorine, near the end of the third period, has a greater electronegativity than sodium, at the beginning. This applies generally: the electronegativities of atoms tend to increase across a period of the Periodic Table. They also usually increase as one moves up a group from the bottom to the top. These trends are explained and marked in Figure 5.6.

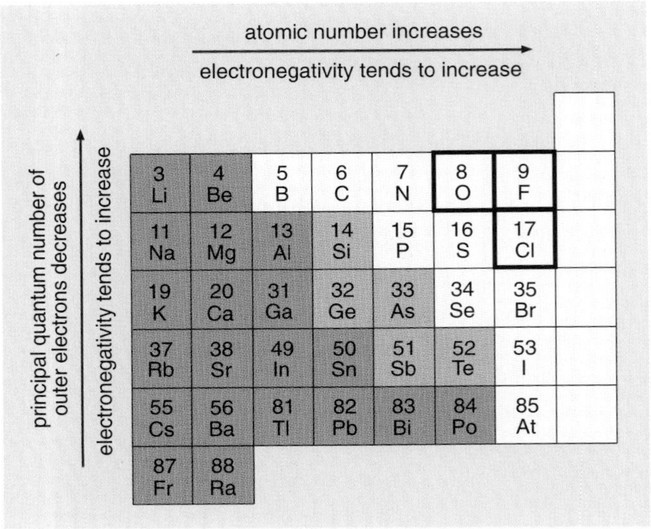

Figure 5.6   Across a period of the Periodic Table, the atomic number, or positive charge on the nucleus increases. This increases the attraction for the outer electrons, so the electronegativity of the elements also tends to increase. As one moves up a group, the principal quantum number of the outer electrons decreases. This means that they get closer to the positively charged nucleus. The result is, again, that the outer electrons are attracted more strongly, and the electronegativity increases. The three most electronegative elements are outlined in black. As in Figure 3.9, hydrogen is omitted because it does not obey these general trends. Its electronegativity is intermediate between a Group I and a Group VII position, and resembles that of carbon.

As Figure 5.6 shows, the result is that the most electronegative elements lie towards the top right-hand corner of the Periodic Table. Electronegativities refer to an attraction for outer electrons when an element is forming compounds. As helium, neon and argon form no compounds, electronegativities are not assigned to them. Consequently, fluorine is the most electronegative element, followed by oxygen and chlorine.

Figure 5.6 therefore confirms that chlorine is much more electronegative than sodium. Because of the large difference in electronegativity, the electrons of the electron pair of Figure 5.5b spend all their time on chlorine, the charges on the particles are $+e$ and $-e$, and NaCl is ionic. So the electronegativity changes in Figure 5.6 explain why ionic compounds arise when a metallic element from the left combines with a non-metallic element from the right. In Cl_2, by contrast, the electronegativity difference between the bound elements is zero; the shared electrons spend equal times on each chlorine atom, both chlorines are uncharged, the substance is held together by covalent bonding and is molecular. So covalently bound molecular substances are combinations from the right of Figure 5.6 because, for these elements, the electronegativity difference is small.

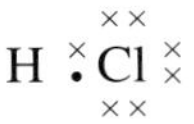

H ːCl

5.6

But what happens at intermediate values of the electronegativity difference? Consider the gas, hydrogen chloride, which consists of HCl molecules and condenses to a colourless, non-conducting liquid at −84 °C. It therefore seems a typical molecular substance, and we represent it as such by writing a Lewis structure (**5.6**) for the molecule.

However, you know of one reaction in which HCl behaves more like an ionic substance.

⬤   What reaction is it?

◯   Like NaCl, it dissolves in water and forms aqueous ions $H^+(aq)$ and $Cl^-(aq)$.

How are we to understand this? Chlorine is a very electronegative element (Figure 5.6), more electronegative than hydrogen, so the electron pair between the atoms spends more time on chlorine than on hydrogen. But it does not spend all its time on chlorine; if that were so, HCl would have the properties of an ionic compound, and we could write it H^+Cl^-. The situation is intermediate between an ionic picture in which hydrogen and chlorine carry charges of $+e$ and $-e$, respectively, and equal sharing of the electron pair with no charge separation. Such intermediate cases can be represented by adding, to the structural formula, symbols that represent a small positive charge on the hydrogen, and an equal but opposite charge on the chlorine, as in structure **5.7**.

$$\overset{\delta+}{H} - \overset{\delta-}{Cl}$$

5.7

The small amounts of charge are called *partial* charges, and written $\delta+$ and $\delta-$, where δ is the Greek lower case letter delta. They arise from an unequal sharing of the electrons in the electron-pair bond. One sign of their presence is that, in water, the charge transfer becomes complete, and HCl gas dissolves to form $H^+(aq)$ and $Cl^-(aq)$ ions. Later in the block, you will see how partial charges caused by electronegativity differences have other important consequences.

5.6   Summary of Section 5

1   The chemical formulae of many substances can be understood by arguing that their atoms attain noble gas electron structures by chemical combination.

2   In ionic compounds, this is achieved by the transfer of electrons from one atom to another; in molecular substances, by the sharing of electron pairs in covalent bonds.

3   The prominent valencies that the non-metallic elements achieve in molecular substances are equal to the number of covalent bonds that they form when they attain noble gas electron structures. Each shared electron pair constitutes a covalent bond. Double bonds, as in CO_2, require two shared pairs; a triple bond, as in N_2, requires three.

4   Whether the bonding in a substance is ionic or covalent is strongly affected by the electronegativities of the atoms of which the substance is composed. Electronegativity is the power of an atom to attract electrons to itself when forming chemical bonds; it increases from left to right across a row of the Periodic Table, and up a column.

5   So when non-metallic elements on the right of the Periodic Table combine with each other, the electronegativity difference is small, and molecular substances are formed; when non-metallic elements on the right combine with metallic elements on the left, the electronegativity difference is large, and ionic compounds are formed.

6   Electronegativity differences between two covalently bound atoms lead to unequal sharing of the electron pair that makes up the bond. This can be acknowledged by placing partial charges, $\delta+$ and $\delta-$, on the less and more electronegative atoms, respectively.

When doing Questions 5.2–5.6, you may find it helpful to refer to the Periodic Table shown in Figure 5.2. This shows the electrons in the outer shell of the atoms.

Notice that Section 5 has left you with three ways of writing the formulae of molecular compounds. There is the ordinary molecular formula (e.g. NCl_3) inherited from Block 6. Then there are the structural formula of structure **4.4** and the Lewis structure (structure **5.3**). Question 5.4 helps you to distinguish the three types. Question 5.5 explains the trend in hydride formulae, which was our most valuable indicator of chemical periodicity in Block 6.

Question 5.2   Lithium and calcium react with nitrogen to form ionic nitrides. If the ions in these compounds have noble gas structures, what are their charges? Predict the formulae of lithium nitride and calcium nitride. ◀

Question 5.3   Oxygen gas and sulfur dichloride contain the molecules O_2 and SCl_2, respectively. Draw a Lewis structure for each molecule. What noble gas structure is achieved by each atom in the molecules? ◀

Question 5.4   Write down the molecular formula, a structural formula and a Lewis structure for each of the gases ammonia and fluorine. ◀

Question 5.5   The formulae of the highest hydrides of the elements of Period 3 of the Periodic Table are NaH, MgH_2, AlH_3, SiH_4, PH_3, H_2S, and HCl. Argon does not form a hydride. The first three hydrides are white solids with structures characteristic of ionic compounds. The remaining substances are molecular gases or liquids at room temperature. Explain their formulae, first by writing down the ions in the ionic compounds, specifying their charges and noble gas structures, and secondly by drawing Lewis structures for the molecular compounds, and specifying the noble gas structure that each atom attains. ◀

Question 5.6   Statements (a)–(c) below describe properties of carbon tetrachloride, CCl_4, oxygen difluoride, OF_2, and potassium oxide, K_2O. These substances are either ionic, or molecular with covalent bonding. Where you think a substance is ionic, assign charges to each ion. Where you think a substance is molecular, draw a Lewis structure. Are your answers consistent with point 5 of the summary above?

(a) CCl_4 is a liquid at room temperature and does not conduct electricity; it boils at 77 °C.

(b) OF_2 is a gas at room temperature.

(c) K_2O is a solid with a high melting temperature. The structure is such that each potassium is surrounded by four oxygens, and each oxygen is surrounded by eight potassiums. ◀

Chemical reactions and energy changes

6

In Sections 2–5 we have begun to 'put the world together', learning about atoms and the bonds that they form with one another in chemical compounds. However, we must also recognize that our world is far from static: it involves change. Indeed, change associated with chemical reactions is of immense utility and interest.

In the next few sections (6 to 11) we take a more detailed look at chemical reactions and the changes that accompany them, starting with energy changes. These can have considerable practical benefit. For instance, most of our daily energy needs are provided, in one way or another, by burning fossil fuels in air (Block 2, Section 6.4). It must be remembered, however, that these fuels, for example natural gas (Figure 6.1), represent non-renewable energy sources and one day they will be exhausted. What remains must be used as efficiently as possible and alternative energy sources need to be developed for the future. Chemistry has a major role to play in achieving these aims.

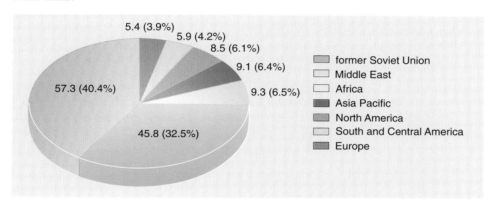

57.3 (40.4%)
5.4 (3.9%)
5.9 (4.2%)
8.5 (6.1%)
9.1 (6.4%)
9.3 (6.5%)
45.8 (32.5%)

former Soviet Union
Middle East
Africa
Asia Pacific
North America
South and Central America
Europe

Figure 6.1 The global proved reserves cf natural gas at the end of 1996, measured in the volume unit 10^{12} m^3. For the United Kingdom the proved reserves are 0.70×10^{12} m^3, and the annual consumption is about one-tenth of this amount.

Activity 6.1   The properties of chemical reactions

In this activity you will study a video sequence 'Features of reactions', which shows a number of chemical reactions. These reactions are not only visually interesting, but also illustrate some of the properties of chemical reactions that you will study in more detail in Sections 6 to 11. ◄

6.1   Chemical change and internal energy

The concept of energy was discussed in detail in Block 5, and you were told that the conversion of any form of energy into any other form is governed by the law of conservation of energy.

⬤ What is the law of conservation of energy?

◯ The total amount of energy is always constant; that is, energy cannot be created or destroyed.

⬤ In the video 'Features of reactions', you saw that various reactions release energy in different forms. What, apart from heat, were these forms?

◯ Light energy (reactions 2 and 4) and electrical energy (reaction 5).

Two reactions in the video involved the release of energy in the form of heat. One was the volcano-like burning of an orange-red solid, ammonium dichromate. The second involved the mixing of two colourless liquids at room temperature with the result that the temperature of the mixture increased significantly. It is important to note that this rise in temperature was *not* caused by any external heating of the reaction mixture.

Where does the energy released by these chemical reactions come from? The law of conservation of energy tells us that chemical reactions cannot *create* energy, and so there must be a *conversion* of one form of energy into another. Energy is released by these reactions because there is a change in internal energy.

You should recall from Block 5 that there are two important components to the internal energy of a substance. One of these is kinetic energy, which is associated with random motion at the molecular level in a substance. The other component is potential energy. This is associated with the forces between particular atoms in a substance that result in the formation of chemical bonds, and also, if appropriate, with the forces between molecules that hold the substance together. In a chemical reaction, chemical bonds in the reactants are broken and new bonds are formed to give rise to the products. The reactants and products are chemically different, and this means that their respective potential energies will be different. This difference in potential energy is the source of the change in internal energy. It is sometimes referred to as a change in chemical energy.

So far, our discussion has focused on chemical reactions that *release* energy. However, in the video you saw an example of a reaction that *absorbed* energy from its local environment (Figure 6.2). As the two solids reacted to produce a liquid product, the puddle of water in which the beaker was standing was turned to ice. For this reaction, therefore, the change in internal energy is in the direction that results in heat being absorbed from the puddle of water, cooling it enough to cause the water to freeze. This reaction is by no means unique; many other chemical reactions absorb energy.

We are now in a position to draw two important conclusions.

Figure 6.2   A still from the video 'Features of reactions', illustrating a reaction in which energy (in the form of heat) is absorbed from the local environment. The watch-glass is attached to the beaker by ice.

> Chemical reactions involve changes in internal energy. These changes can result in either release of energy to, or absorption of energy from, the local environment.

6.2   Chemical reactions that release or absorb heat

The fact that a large proportion of chemical reactions involve either the release, or absorption, of energy in the form of heat suggests that it is worthwhile classifying reactions on this basis. Before doing so, however, it is useful to introduce two terms: **system** and **surroundings**. For our purposes, we can think of the system as being the contents of a reaction mixture. The surroundings is literally *everything* else, but to be more practical it could simply be a beaker and the air (or water) in the immediate vicinity. We shall make use of both of these terms in due course, but for now we need only use the term 'surroundings' explicitly.

Reactions are classified as follows:

A chemical reaction that releases heat into the surroundings is called an **exothermic reaction**.

A chemical reaction that absorbs heat from the surroundings is called an **endothermic reaction**.

The terms exothermic and endothermic come from the Greek: *thermo* meaning heat, *exo* meaning outside, and *endo* meaning within. Hence *exo*thermic conveys the idea that heat is given *out* and *endo*thermic that heat is taken *in*. You should note that this classification takes no account of the time-scale of a chemical reaction. Thus a reaction, for example rusting, that occurs so slowly that the heat released is hardly noticeable is classified as exothermic in exactly the same way as a reaction that causes flames.

Question 6.1   Immediate first-aid for a strain or sprain caused by playing sport often consists of cooling the damaged area. One way of doing this is with a 'cold pack' that effectively consists of a plastic bag divided into two compartments — one containing a soluble solid and the other water. The partition in the bag is broken (by squeezing) and the bag is then placed against the injury to achieve the desired cooling effect.

(a) Briefly explain how you think that the pack works.

(b) Can you suggest a design for a 'hot pack', that sports' fans might appreciate on a cold winter's afternoon? ◄

6.3   Quantitative information: enthalpy changes

So far, we have considered only general aspects of the energy changes associated with chemical reactions. However, quantitative information concerning the amount of energy released or absorbed by a chemical reaction under a given set of circumstances is of considerable practical interest. For example, the ability to compare the merits of different fuels in terms of the energy they release when burned is clearly important.

To begin our discussion we shall take as an example the reaction between magnesium metal and fluorine gas, which was shown in the CD-ROM activity in Block 6. This reaction is very vigorous and the reaction mixture bursts into flames. It can be described qualitatively as follows:

$$Mg(s) + F_2(g) \longrightarrow MgF_2(s) + energy \tag{6.1}$$

This indicates that the reaction is exothermic: energy in the form of heat is transferred to the surroundings. This is because the product — solid magnesium fluoride — has a *lower* internal energy than the combined internal energies of the reactants — magnesium metal and fluorine gas. A schematic view of the energy changes in the reaction is shown in Figure 6.3.

In practice, when an exothermic reaction occurs it normally raises the temperature of the reaction mixture, that is the system. However, after a time, heat will flow from the system to the surroundings until the products are at the same temperature as the reactants were at the start. For example, when the solid magnesium fluoride in

Figure 6.3 A schematic view of the energy changes that occur when magnesium metal reacts with fluorine gas. Notice that the vertical axis represents energy, increasing upwards.

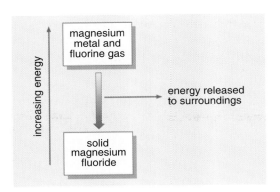

Figure 6.3 has cooled to the same temperature as the magnesium metal and fluorine gas were at the start, *all* of the energy released in the form of heat will have been transferred to the surroundings. The overall effect is exactly the same as it would have been if the reaction had occurred throughout at a *constant temperature* equal to that of the reactants at the start of the reaction. This observation suggests a useful and unambiguous way to do energy accounting. If we state that an exothermic reaction has occurred at constant temperature then we are indicating that all of the energy released in the form of heat has been transferred to the surroundings.

Question 6.2   Read the last paragraph again and then, without further reference, develop a similar account for an endothermic reaction. ◀

More often than not, chemical reactions are carried out in containers that are open to the atmosphere. In effect the reactions are being carried out under *constant pressure* conditions. This was the case, for example, for all of the reactions you viewed in Activity 6.1.

The condition of constant pressure needs exploring in a little more depth. The reason for this can be appreciated by considering a simple example. If a chemical reaction in solution results in the formation of a gaseous product, then part of the internal energy change for this reaction will be expended in pushing back the atmosphere in order to 'make space' for the gas formed. So, if the reaction is exothermic, then the energy released as heat will be less than the overall internal energy change for the reaction. In general, for any reaction that occurs at constant pressure and involves a volume change, there will be a difference between the change in internal energy and the energy released (or absorbed) as heat. These differences are generally very small; the exceptions are reactions involving gases, in which there can be significant volume changes.

In most practical situations, it is the energy released, or absorbed, in the form of heat by a chemical reaction that is of direct interest. For any chemical reaction occurring at *constant pressure* this particular form of energy transfer can be identified with a change in a property called **enthalpy**. For a given substance the enthalpy can be thought of as a kind of energy store that provides, or accepts, energy in the form of heat. This idea is reflected in the derivation of the term — it comes from the Greek words for 'heat inside'.

The symbol that it is given to enthalpy is H, and an **enthalpy change** is written as ΔH, where the Greek capital letter Δ (spoken delta) means 'change of'. (You first met this notation in Block 5.) Because an enthalpy change represents heat transferred, the appropriate SI unit is the joule. For a chemical reaction occurring at constant pressure and constant temperature:

$$\Delta H = H(\text{products}) - H(\text{reactants}) \tag{6.2}$$

This equation says that the heat released, or absorbed, by the reaction is equal to the difference between the enthalpy of the products and the enthalpy of the reactants. Although we shall not go into detail, such enthalpy changes can be measured experimentally.

> The enthalpy change for any chemical reaction occurring at constant pressure and constant temperature can be taken as a direct measure of the energy released, or absorbed, in the form of heat alone.

The sign of ΔH can be determined from Equation 6.2.

● Will ΔH be positive or negative for an exothermic reaction?

○ An exothermic reaction is one that releases energy in the form of heat to the surroundings. This must mean that the enthalpy of the products is less than the enthalpy of the reactants. Thus ΔH will have a *negative* value.

For an endothermic reaction, the enthalpy of the products is greater than the enthalpy of the reactants, and ΔH has a positive value.

Note that the sign of ΔH reflects what is happening to the system, that is the reaction mixture itself. Thus for an exothermic reaction the system releases energy in the form of heat *to* the surroundings and so, in effect, ends up *minus* some energy. In contrast, for an endothermic reaction the system gains energy in the form of heat *from* the surroundings and so, in effect, ends up *plus* some energy.

> For an exothermic reaction ΔH is negative.
>
> For an endothermic reaction ΔH is positive.

An alternative way of depicting enthalpy changes for chemical reactions occurring at constant pressure and constant temperature is via enthalpy diagrams, as shown in Figure 6.4.

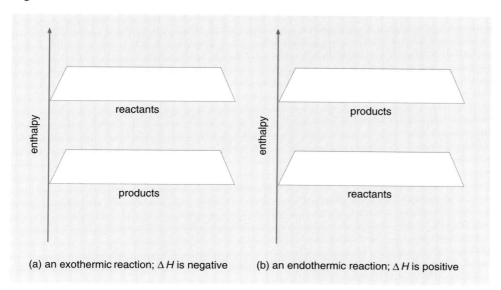

(a) an exothermic reaction; ΔH is negative   (b) an endothermic reaction; ΔH is positive

Figure 6.4 Enthalpy diagrams for (a) an exothermic reaction and (b) an endothermic reaction. The vertical axes represent enthalpy, increasing upwards, and the enthalpies of reactants and the enthalpies of products are represented by different levels on the axes.

6.3.1 Thermochemical equations

We are now in a position to look at the energy changes associated with chemical reactions in a more quantitative manner. Because it is the heat that is released or absorbed that is of most practical interest, our discussion will focus on enthalpy changes. We start by considering enthalpy changes associated with changes of state.

Changes of state

The vaporization of water, at atmospheric pressure and at its boiling temperature of 100 °C, was discussed in some detail in Block 5. In fact, this change of state can be represented by a chemical equation:

$$H_2O(l) \longrightarrow H_2O(g) \qquad (6.3)$$

○ Is this change of state an exothermic or endothermic process?

○ As you should recall from Block 5, energy in the form of heat has to be supplied to vaporize a liquid. In other words, the change of state requires absorption of heat from the surroundings at constant temperature (100 °C). Hence, it is endothermic.

○ Block 5 used a particular term to describe the energy required to vaporize a unit mass of a liquid at its boiling temperature. What is this term?

○ It is the latent heat of vaporization, L.

The latent heat of vaporization of water is $2.26 \times 10^6\,J\,kg^{-1}$. This quantity refers to the change of state occurring. not only at constant temperature, but also at constant (atmospheric) pressure. It is thus equivalent to an enthalpy change. This particular enthalpy change is often referred to as the **enthalpy of vaporization** and is represented as ΔH(vaporization), or just ΔH(vap) for short. Hence, we can write ΔH(vap) = $+ 2.26 \times 10^6\,J\,kg^{-1}$, where the positive sign has been included because the change is endothermic. It is generally the case that enthalpy changes are reported in kilojoules, kJ, rather than joules; $1\,kJ = 1.0 \times 10^3\,J$. Thus, to be more conventional, we write ΔH(vap) = $+2\,260\,kJ\,kg^{-1}$. This means that an enthalpy change of $+2\,260\,kJ$ occurs when 1 kg of liquid water, at 100 °C and at atmospheric pressure, is completely converted into water vapour (steam).

It is also useful to express enthalpy changes in molar terms, because a direct link can then be made with the corresponding chemical equation interpreted on a molar basis.

○ How would you interpret Equation 6.3 on a molar basis?

○ It can be interpreted as indicating that one mole of water molecules in the liquid state is converted into one mole of water molecules in the gaseous (or vapour) state.

Question 6.3 Calculate a value for the enthalpy of vaporization for one mole of water molecules, given that ΔH(vap) = $+2\,260\,kJ\,kg^{-1}$. (You will need first to work out the mass of one mole of water molecules. Take the relative atomic masses of hydrogen and oxygen to be 1.01 and 16.0, respectively.) ◀

The enthalpy of vaporization of water calculated in Question 6.3 can be combined with the chemical equation (6.3) to give a **thermochemical equation** for the vaporization of water:

$$H_2O(l) \longrightarrow H_2O(g) \qquad \Delta H\text{(vap)} = + 40.7\,kJ \qquad (6.4)$$

This thermochemical equation conveniently combines the chemical equation, *which is to be interpreted on a molar basis*, with a statement of the corresponding enthalpy change. We shall use this type of equation throughout the remainder of this block.

We can also write a thermochemical equation for condensation, which is the reverse of vaporization. Because vaporization involves the *absorption* of a given amount of energy in the form of heat, then it follows from the law of conservation of energy that this same amount of heat will be *released* on condensation. Hence, condensation is an exothermic process.

● Write down the thermochemical equation that describes one mole of water molecules in the gaseous state condensing to give liquid water at 100 °C and atmospheric pressure.

○ The thermochemical equation is:

$$H_2O(g) \longrightarrow H_2O(l) \quad \Delta H(\text{condensation}) = -40.7 \, \text{kJ} \tag{6.5}$$

Question 6.4   Scalding by steam is extremely painful. Give a brief description of what happens in energy terms when steam comes into contact with skin. ◀

Chemical reactions

The idea of a thermochemical equation is quite general. The reaction between magnesium metal and fluorine gas, for instance, gives rise to the following thermochemical equation:

$$Mg(s) + F_2(g) \longrightarrow MgF_2(s) \quad \Delta H = -1\,123 \, \text{kJ} \tag{6.6}$$

This equation can be 'read' as follows: 'when one mole of magnesium atoms in solid magnesium reacts with one mole of fluorine molecules in the gaseous state at constant pressure to form solid magnesium fluoride at the same temperature, 1 123 kJ of energy in the form of heat are transferred from the system to the surroundings'. Although expressed in molar terms, the thermochemical equation can be used to calculate the heat released when any amount of magnesium metal reacts with fluorine gas.

● How much energy in the form of heat will be released when 5.00 g of magnesium metal react with fluorine gas at constant pressure? (The relative atomic mass of magnesium is 24.3.)

○ According to the thermochemical equation, the reaction of one mole of magnesium atoms, that is 24.3 g of magnesium, results in the release of 1 123 kJ of energy in the form of heat.

So 1 g of magnesium will release $\frac{1123}{24.3}$ kJ. If 5.00 g of magnesium react, then the energy released in the form of heat will be:

$$\frac{1\,123 \times 5.00}{24.3} \, \text{kJ} = 231 \, \text{kJ}$$

Thermochemical equations are particularly useful for comparing chemical reactions of the same type. An important set of reactions are those in which different fuels are burned in oxygen (usually from the air). For example, the thermochemical equations for burning hydrogen gas and methane gas are as follows:

$$2H_2(g) + O_2(g) \longrightarrow 2H_2O(g) \quad \Delta H = -484 \, \text{kJ} \tag{6.7}$$

$$CH_4(g) + 2O_2(g) \longrightarrow CO_2(g) + 2H_2O(g) \quad \Delta H = -802 \, \text{kJ} \tag{6.8}$$

Comparison of the two equations tells us that completely burning *one* mole of methane gas releases significantly more energy in the form of heat than does burning *two* moles of hydrogen gas. However, we don't usually buy fuel by the mole — and a more usual, and practical, way of comparing the heat released by different fuels is on a mass-for-mass basis.

Table 6.1 provides the thermochemical equations for a wider selection of fuels: those used in our homes, motor cars, industry, or our own bodies. Petrol is a complex mixture and so information for the 'representative' compound, octane, is given; the balanced chemical equation is quite complex in this case. The chemical formulae given in the table are written in a way that you will learn more about in Section 12. The final column in the table gives, for each fuel apart from ethanol, a value for the energy released as heat when 1 kg of the fuel is fully burned in oxygen. For convenience, these values are expressed to the nearest thousand kilojoules.

Table 6.1   Fuels and the energy they release as heat.

Fuel	Thermochemical equation		Energy released as heat per kilogram of fuel/kJ
carbon, C (as in coal)	$C(s) + O_2(g) \longrightarrow CO_2(g)$	$\Delta H = -394 \text{ kJ}$	33 000
methane, CH_4 (as in natural gas)	$CH_4(g) + 2O_2(g) \longrightarrow CO_2(g) + 2H_2O(g)$	$\Delta H = -802 \text{ kJ}$	50 000
octane, C_8H_{18} (as in petrol)	$2C_8H_{18}(l) + 25O_2(g) \longrightarrow$ $16CO_2(g) + 18H_2O(g)$	$\Delta H = -10\,240 \text{ kJ}$	45 000
methanol, CH_3OH	$2CH_3OH(l) + 3O_2(g) \longrightarrow$ $2CO_2(g) + 4H_2O(g)$	$\Delta H = -1\,277 \text{ kJ}$	20 000
ethanol, C_2H_5OH	$C_2H_5OH(l) + 3O_2(g) \longrightarrow$ $2CO_2(g) + 3H_2O(g)$	$\Delta H = -1\,238 \text{ kJ}$	
carbohydrates (sugars and starches)	products are $CO_2(g)$ and $H_2O(l)$		an average value of 17 000
animal fats	products are $CO_2(g)$ and $H_2O(l)$		variable; 40 000 a typical value
hydrogen, H_2	$2H_2(g) + O_2(g) \longrightarrow 2H_2O(g)$	$\Delta H = -484 \text{ kJ}$	120 000

Question 6.5   To complete Table 6.1, calculate the energy released as heat when 1 kg of liquid ethanol is fully burned in oxygen. ◀

A vision of the future called 'The hydrogen economy' was discussed in Block 6, Box 3.2. On a mass-for-mass basis, hydrogen gas is potentially a very good fuel and, in principle, it could be distributed via a pipeline system to where energy is needed. A further advantage is that it is the only fuel in Table 6.1 that does not give rise to carbon dioxide emissions and thus to concern about global warming. But there are also significant drawbacks. A major problem is that there is little hydrogen on Earth that is not tied up in chemical compounds. Hydrogen has to be treated as a synthetic fuel that has to be manufactured, for example from water. This can be done only at significant cost. Combustion of hydrogen in air also occurs at temperatures at which nitrogen will react with oxygen to produce a harmful mix of nitrogen oxide gases; in environmental terms it is not a 'clean' process. Other points can also be made, for example, with regard to safety; a spark in the wrong place could be disastrous (to which the *Hindenburg* disaster of 1937 is testimony). It is also important to recognize that hydrogen has the lowest density of any gas and so a given volume will have a relatively small mass. It turns out that, on a *volume-for-volume* basis, the energy released as heat by burning hydrogen amounts to roughly one-third of that released by burning natural gas.

Activity 6.2   An alternative to petrol

In this activity you are asked to suggest factors that should be taken into account in considering ethanol as an alternative to petrol as a fuel for motor vehicles. You will then compare your suggestions with those in a published article. ◀

6.4   Enthalpy changes: delving deeper

The enthalpy changes that have been quoted in thermochemical equations so far have all been measured experimentally. However, *for reactions in which the reactants and products are all gases*, it is often possible to estimate the magnitudes of enthalpy changes without recourse to experiment. The method of estimation provides us with a means of delving deeper into the source of the enthalpy change for a given reaction.

Underlying the method of estimation is an important property of the enthalpy change for any reaction occurring at constant pressure and constant temperature. The enthalpy change is *independent* of the way in which the reaction occurs. The starting reactants have a certain enthalpy, and so do the final products. The change is simply equal to the difference. You can think of this as being rather like travelling between two places; there may be a number of different routes but you will always finish up the same distance, as the crow flies, from your starting point.

As an example of estimating an enthalpy change we shall consider the reaction between hydrogen gas and oxygen gas:

$$2H_2(g) + O_2(g) \longrightarrow 2H_2O(g) \tag{6.9}$$

Let's imagine this reaction occurring in a simple two-step sequence. In step 1, we can imagine that the covalent bonds in the diatomic hydrogen and oxygen molecules are broken so that individual hydrogen and oxygen atoms are formed.

$$\text{step 1:} \quad 2H_2(g) + O_2(g) \longrightarrow 4H(g) + 2O(g) \tag{6.10}$$

In step 2 the hydrogen and oxygen atoms combine to form water molecules.

$$\text{step 2:} \quad 4H(g) + 2O(g) \longrightarrow 2H_2O(g) \tag{6.11}$$

Equations 6.10 and 6.11 are both to be interpreted on a *molar basis*. The overall reaction, which we know is exothermic (Table 6.1), can be represented by the enthalpy diagram in Figure 6.5.

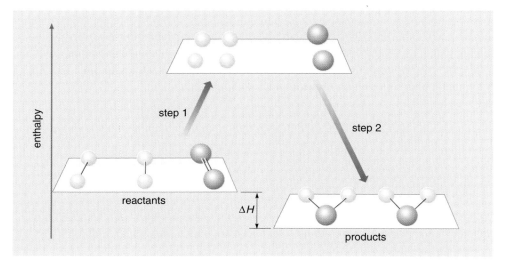

Figure 6.5   An enthalpy diagram showing the two-step sequence we have selected to represent how the reaction between $H_2(g)$ and $O_2(g)$ occurs so that $H_2O(g)$ is produced. For simplicity, just two molecules of hydrogen (grey) are shown reacting with one molecule of oxygen (red).

Remember that this two-step sequence need *not* represent how the reaction between hydrogen gas and oxygen gas actually occurs. In fact, it is known that this reaction occurs in a longer sequence of steps.

The breakdown of hydrogen, oxygen or indeed any diatomic molecule in the gaseous state into its constituent atoms is referred to as dissociation.

⬤ Would you expect dissociation to be an exothermic or endothermic process?

◯ If you imagine the process occurring at constant temperature, then energy in the form of heat will have to be supplied in order to break the covalent bonds. So dissociation is an endothermic process.

The thermochemical equations for the dissociation of hydrogen and oxygen are as follows:

$$H_2(g) \longrightarrow H(g) + H(g) \qquad \Delta H = +436 \, kJ \tag{6.12}$$

$$O_2(g) \longrightarrow O(g) + O(g) \qquad \Delta H = +498 \, kJ \tag{6.13}$$

The enthalpy change in each of these two equations is called the **molar bond enthalpy**. This term is general and applies to the dissociation of all diatomic molecules. Because the dissociation process is always endothermic, molar bond enthalpies are always positive.

⬤ What is the total enthalpy change for the process we have labelled as step 1?

◯ It is important to consider the number of bonds that are broken. Thus, there are 'two moles of hydrogen–hydrogen bonds' (each mole requiring 436 kJ) and 'one mole of oxygen–oxygen bonds' (requiring 498 kJ). Thus, for step 1, the total enthalpy change amounts to:

$2 \times (+436 \, kJ) + 498 \, kJ = +1\,370 \, kJ$

We now need to consider step 2, in which chemical bonds are formed.

⬤ Would you expect the formation of a chemical bond between two atoms to be an exothermic or endothermic process?

◯ Since bond breaking is endothermic, then it must be the case that the reverse process, bond formation, is exothermic. (There are parallels here with the discussion of the vaporization and condensation of water in Section 6.3.1.)

It is important to be clear about the details of the argument at this stage. The breaking of 'one mole of chemical bonds' is an endothermic process and has an enthalpy change given by the molar bond enthalpy. The reverse process — the formation of 'one mole of chemical bonds' — is exothermic and will have an enthalpy change that is simply the negative of the molar bond enthalpy.

⬤ The mean molar bond enthalpy for each of the two O—H bonds[*] in the water molecule is 463 kJ. What is the total enthalpy change for step 2? (Consider the number of bonds that are formed.)

[*] The water molecule contains two oxygen–hydrogen, O—H, bonds. In this case the idea of bond enthalpy still holds but it refers to breaking *just one* of these bonds. In fact, the situation is a little more complex than it might seem. If the two O—H bonds in the water molecule are broken one after another, then the enthalpy changes for these two processes treated separately are not equal. However, for the purposes of our calculation it is reasonable to take a mean of these enthalpy changes.

○ In one mole of water molecules there are 'two moles of O—H bonds'. However, *two* moles of water molecules are formed. This is equivalent to the formation of 'four moles of O—H bonds', each mole of which releases 463 kJ. Thus, for step 2, the enthalpy change amounts to:

$$4 \times (-463) \, \text{kJ} = -1 \, 852 \, \text{kJ}$$

Our calculations, so far, have been based on the separate reactions in Equations 6.10 and 6.11.

● What happens if these equations are added together?

○ The addition gives:

$$2H_2(g) + O_2(g) + 4H(g) + 2O(g) \longrightarrow 4H(g) + 2O(g) + 2H_2O(g) \qquad (6.14)$$

Cancelling out the compounds that are the same on both sides of this equation gives the equation for the overall reaction, that is:

$$2H_2(g) + O_2(g) \longrightarrow 2H_2O(g) \qquad (6.9)$$

In the same way, the overall enthalpy change for the reaction is found by adding together the enthalpy changes for the individual steps:

$$\Delta H = \Delta H(\text{step 1}) + \Delta H(\text{step 2}) \qquad (6.15)$$

● What is the overall enthalpy change, in kilojoules?

○ $\Delta H = +1 \, 370 \, \text{kJ} + (-1 \, 852 \, \text{kJ})$

$= +1 \, 370 \, \text{kJ} - 1 \, 852 \, \text{kJ}$

$= -482 \, \text{kJ}$

This value is negative, showing that the reaction is exothermic, and it agrees well with the experimental value in Table 6.1, that is -484 kJ.

So, what can we now say about the enthalpy changes that occur during a chemical reaction? Our two-step sequence for the reaction between hydrogen gas and oxygen gas was deliberately chosen to be simple. Nonetheless, no matter how a chemical reaction occurs in practice, chemical bonds must always be broken and new ones formed between different partners. It is this 'breaking and making' of chemical bonds that makes a major contribution to the overall enthalpy change and, indeed, can determine whether a reaction is exothermic or endothermic. Estimates of enthalpy changes are generally restricted to reactions in which the reactants and products are all gases; that is, to reactions that occur in the gas phase.

Question 6.6   Hydrogen gas reacts with chlorine gas as follows:

$$H_2(g) + Cl_2(g) \longrightarrow 2HCl(g)$$

The molar bond enthalpies for the H—H, Cl—Cl and H—Cl chemical bonds are 436 kJ, 242 kJ and 431 kJ, respectively. Use this information to estimate the overall enthalpy change for the reaction. Is the reaction exothermic or endothermic? ◀

6.5   Summary of Section 6

1   Chemical reactions involve changes in internal energy.

2   A chemical reaction that releases heat into the surroundings is called exothermic; one that absorbs heat from the surroundings is called endothermic.

3   For a reaction that occurs at constant pressure and constant temperature, the enthalpy change ΔH can be taken as a measure of the exchange of energy in the form of heat with the surroundings. For an exothermic reaction the value of ΔH is negative, and for an endothermic reaction the value of ΔH is positive.

4   The enthalpy change for a chemical reaction can be represented using an enthalpy diagram.

5   A thermochemical equation combines the chemical equation, which is to be interpreted on a molar basis, with a statement of the corresponding enthalpy change.

6   Enthalpy changes for reactions occurring in the gas phase can be estimated using molar bond enthalpies.

Water

We started *Discovering Science* by looking in Block 1 at one specific substance — water. In Block 2 we saw the important role of the water cycle on the Earth. Here, we begin to explore the role that water plays in chemistry. In particular, we examine its ability to act as a solvent, and this will allow us to gain a better understanding of reactions that occur in solution, which is one of the tasks of Sections 8 to 10. Two other important properties of water that we will discuss are its boiling and melting temperatures, which ensure that it occurs in the liquid form over most of the Earth.

7.1 Solubility in water

As you saw in Block 6, a substance (the solute) dissolves in a solvent to form a solution. The most common solutions are those that result from a solid dissolving in a liquid, such as sugar or salt dissolving in water. But this is not always the case; sometimes liquids dissolve in other liquids, for example, alcohol will dissolve in water. Water also dissolves gases, such as oxygen, nitrogen and carbon dioxide to limited extents, and, as you saw in Block 1 Section 6, the presence of dissolved oxygen in water is a prerequisite for most aquatic life.

Before examining the solvent properties of water, it is important to remind you of a critical property of the water molecule — its shape. You saw in Block 2 Section 6 that the three atoms in a water molecule are joined together as shown in Figure 7.1, not in a straight line. Thus the water molecule can be described as being 'V-shaped', and this shape has a significant influence on its properties.

7.1.1 Why do substances dissolve in water?

In Section 4 you saw that ionic compounds dissolve in water but not in some other solvents, such as petrol and dry-cleaning fluid. In the solid form, an ionic compound exists as a three-dimensional arrangement of positive and negative ions. In general, each positive ion tends to be surrounded by negative ions and each negative ion by positive ions (Figure 4.4). When an ionic compound dissolves in water, the ions become separated from one another and, as a consequence, they become surrounded by water molecules.

- A water molecule has two hydrogen atoms bonded to an oxygen atom. Focusing on just one of the hydrogen–oxygen bonds, how will the electron pair be shared? What will be the partial charges on the hydrogen atom and the oxygen atom, respectively?

- As you saw in Figure 5.6, oxygen is one of the three most electronegative elements, so the electrons between the atoms will spend more time close to the oxygen atom than close to the hydrogen atom. Thus the hydrogen atom will have a small excess of positive charge and the oxygen atom a small excess of negative charge.

The electron pairs are shared unequally in *both* of the hydrogen–oxygen bonds in a water molecule. This results in the distribution of charge shown in Figure 7.2. When an ionic compound dissolves in water, therefore, the positive ions become surrounded by the negatively charged oxygen atoms of the water molecules, and the negative ions become surrounded by the positively charged hydrogen atoms of other water molecules. This is shown schematically in Figure 7.3.

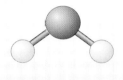

Figure 7.1   A ball-and-stick representation of a water molecule. The angle between the two O—H bonds is about 105°.

Figure 7.2   The charge distribution in a water molecule. There is a partial positive charge on each hydrogen and a partial negative charge on the oxygen. The symbol, δ, simply indicates that the charges are small; it should not be taken to indicate a specific magnitude of charge. Overall the water molecule is neutral, because the small positive and negative charges cancel each other.

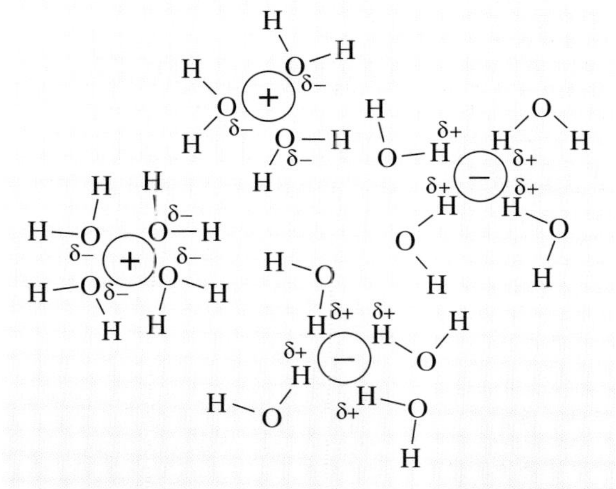

Figure 7.3 When an ionic compound dissolves in water, the negative ions that surround a positive ion in the solid state are replaced by the negatively charged oxygen atoms, $O^{\delta-}$, of water molecules. Likewise, the positive ions that surround a negative ion in the solid state are replaced by the positively charged hydrogen atoms, $H^{\delta+}$, of water molecules. (For clarity, only the partial charges adjacent to the ions are shown.)

A factor that is important when ionic compounds dissolve in water is that one set of attractive interactions is replaced by another. In an ionic compound there are attractive interactions between the positively and negatively charged ions. Once the compound is dissolved in water, these interactions are replaced by attractive interactions between individual ions and the oppositely charged regions of surrounding water molecules. Molecules of solvents such as petrol and dry cleaning fluid do not contain regions that are sufficiently positively, or negatively, charged to provide adequate 'replacement' attractive interactions, and as a consequence these liquids are not good solvents for ionic compounds.

Although many compounds dissolve in water, they do so to only a certain extent. So, if you gradually add a compound to water at a particular temperature, eventually a point is reached where no more will dissolve. The solution is then said to be **saturated**. To provide a definition: a solution is saturated when, in the presence of undissolved solute, no more solute will dissolve at that particular temperature. This, in turn, leads to a definition for the **solubility** of a solute: this is the maximum amount of a solute that will dissolve in a given amount of solvent at a particular temperature. A common way of expressing solubility in water is to quote the maximum mass of solute that will dissolve in 100 g of water at a particular temperature. For example, the solubility of sodium chloride in water at 20 °C is 36.0 g of sodium chloride in 100 g of water.

The solubilities of solids usually increase with temperature; for example, more sugar will dissolve in hot tea than in cold water. Thus, whenever a solubility is quoted, it is important that the temperature is also stated.

● At 90 °C, the solubility of sodium nitrate in water is 150 g in 100 g of water. At 25 °C, the solubility is reduced to 90 g in 100 g of water. What happens when a saturated solution of sodium nitrate prepared from 100 g of water at 90 °C cools to 25 °C?

○ As it cools the solution can contain less and less dissolved sodium nitrate, so more and more will separate out from the solution as crystals. At 25 °C only 90 g of sodium nitrate will remain in solution. This means that 150 g – 90 g = 60 g of sodium nitrate will crystallize out. You saw this happen in the Block 6 video 'Introducing chemistry' (Activity 2.1).

The formation of a solid upon cooling of a saturated solution is known as crystallization, and in Block 6 you saw how the process was used to extract sodium nitrate from caliche. It can also provide an important method of purifying solids. For example, the production of refined sugar involves heating sugar cane or sugar beet in hot water. The sugar in the plant material dissolves in the hot water along with other compounds. On cooling, the sugar crystallizes, leaving most of the 'impurities' still dissolved in the water. This process is repeated, giving less contaminated samples each time, until eventually a pure white crystalline product is isolated.

⬤ Why do you think that on cooling only the sugar crystallizes and not the impurities?

◯ On cooling, only the sugar forms a saturated solution, leading to formation of sugar crystals. None of the impurities forms saturated solutions on cooling and thus they all remain in solution.

7.1.2 A dynamic solution

When sodium chloride is added to water, ions close to the surface of the solid break away and become part of the solution. If less sodium chloride is added than is required to produce a saturated solution at a particular temperature, then eventually it all dissolves. We can represent this by the equation:

$$NaCl(s) \longrightarrow Na^+(aq) + Cl^-(aq) \tag{7.1}$$

If the amount of sodium chloride added is greater than that required to produce a saturated solution, the sodium chloride will initially dissolve, but eventually the solution will become saturated. In this case, some undissolved solid will remain at the bottom of the vessel. Providing the temperature and the amount of water remain constant, the amount of solid sodium chloride and the amount of sodium chloride in solution will not change, no matter how long we may wait. The system has achieved a steady state.

However, although the solution may look static, at the atomic level there is continuous change. We can demonstrate the dynamic nature of the situation using a simple experiment. Naturally occurring sodium consists of almost 100% of the isotope ^{23}Na. However, it is possible to make sodium chloride containing the radioactive isotope ^{24}Na, which behaves chemically just like ordinary sodium chloride; but, because of their radioactivity, the $^{24}Na^+(aq)$ ions can be detected using a Geiger counter.

Now suppose we add some solid $^{24}NaCl$ to a saturated solution of sodium chloride in water. The white solid $^{24}NaCl$ joins the other undissolved sodium chloride at the bottom of the vessel, but nothing much else seems to happen. However, if after a while the solid is filtered off, the remaining solution is found to be radioactive.

⬤ On addition of $^{24}NaCl$ there was no increase in the total amount of sodium chloride *in solution*, so how is the radioactivity of the filtered solution explained?

◯ Some $^{24}NaCl$ must have dissolved so that radioactive sodium ions, $^{24}Na^+(aq)$, are present in solution. This process must have been balanced by sodium chloride, containing the common sodium isotope, ^{23}Na, separating out from the solution as crystals. The situation is illustrated in Figure 7.4.

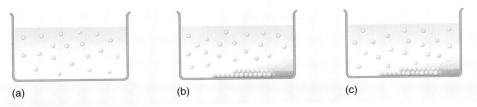

(a)   (b)   (c)

Figure 7.4   (a) A saturated solution of sodium chloride: the sodium ions are shown as grey and the chloride ions as green. (b) The same solution immediately after the addition of ^{24}NaCl: the radioactive sodium ions are shown as red. (c) After some time the amount of sodium chloride in solution has not changed, even though ^{24}Na$^+$ ions have moved from the solid state into solution. This is because the movement is balanced by a corresponding movement of non-radioactive ^{23}Na$^+$ ions from the solution to the solid state.

Thus there are two distinct processes occurring. One is the dissolution of sodium chloride:

$$NaCl(s) \longrightarrow Na^+(aq) + Cl^-(aq) \tag{7.1}$$

The other is the reverse of this process:

$$Na^+(aq) + Cl^-(aq) \longrightarrow NaCl(s) \tag{7.2}$$

Since there is no net change in the amount of sodium chloride in solution or in the amount remaining as solid, we can conclude that the rates of these two processes are the same. This state of dynamic balance is called **chemical equilibrium**. To highlight the two-way nature of equilibrium in chemical equations we use two half-headed arrows pointing in opposite directions, thus:

$$NaCl(s) \rightleftharpoons Na^+(aq) + Cl^-(aq) \tag{7.3}$$

The idea of equilibrium is fundamental to our understanding of chemical reactions:

> When a reaction is in equilibrium, the forward reaction (left to right) and the reverse reaction (right to left) proceed at equal rates.

Question 7.1   At room temperature, about 8.0×10^{-4} g of oxygen gas will dissolve in 100 g of water. This is roughly twice the minimum required to support aquatic life. Oxygen dissolved in water can be represented as $O_2(aq)$. How would you interpret the following equation?

$$O_2(g) \rightleftharpoons O_2(aq) \blacktriangleleft$$

7.1.3   Concentration

Earlier, we expressed solubility in water in terms of the maximum mass of a substance that will dissolve in 100 g of water at a particular temperature. However, it is often more useful to be able to express the amount of solute that is dissolved in *a specific volume of solution*, at a particular temperature. This is known as the **concentration** of the solution. Typically, the concentration is expressed as the amount of solute in one litre of solution. Thus if 10.0 g of sodium chloride are dissolved in water to give 1.0 litre of solution, the concentration is 10.0 g litre^{-1}.

⬤ What is the concentration of a sodium chloride solution if 100 g of NaCl are dissolved in water to give 1.0 litre of solution?

○ The concentration is 100 g litre^{-1}.

Notice we have been careful to define the concentration as the amount of solute in 1.0 litre of the *final* solution rather than the amount of solute dissolved in 1.0 litre of water. If we dissolve 100 g of sodium chloride in 1.0 litre of water at room temperature, the final volume is *greater* than 1.0 litre: it is 1.032 litres. In fact, the final volume depends not only on the amount of the solute but also on the solute itself. For example, if we dissolve 100 g of sodium nitrate in 1.0 litre of water at room temperature, the final volume is 1.036 litres, which is 4 cm^3 more than the volume of the solution of 100 g of sodium chloride in 1.0 litre of water. So to make up a solution with a particular concentration of a solute, the required amount of solute is dissolved in a suitable amount of water and then sufficient water is added to ensure that the correct final volume is achieved.

⬤ A solution is made by dissolving 25 g of sodium chloride in sufficient water to make 1.0 litre of solution. If 100 cm^3 of this solution are then poured into a beaker, what is the mass of sodium chloride contained in this 100 cm^3 of solution?

◯ One way of tackling this problem is to notice that 1.0 litre contains 1 000 cm^3 and that 100 cm^3 is $\frac{100}{1000}$, that is one-tenth the volume of the original solution. Thus it will contain one-tenth of 25 g, that is $\frac{25\,g}{10}$ = 2.5 g, of sodium chloride.

However, not all volumes dispensed from a solution will be simple fractions of a litre. A more general way of performing the calculation is to work out how many grams of sodium chloride are dissolved in 1 cm^3 of solution and then scale up to the appropriate amount. For example, the solution has a concentration of 25 g litre^{-1} and one litre is the same as 1 000 cm^3. Thus in 1 cm^3 of solution there is $\frac{25\,g}{1000}$ = 0.025 g of sodium chloride. We have 100 cm^3 of this solution, thus it contains 100×0.025 g = 2.5 g of sodium chloride.

⬤ What is the mass of sodium chloride contained in 60 cm^3 of this solution?

◯ In 1 cm^3 there is $\frac{25\,g}{1000}$ = 0.025 g. So 60 cm^3 of this solution thus contain 60×0.025 g = 1.5 g of sodium chloride.

⬤ What is the concentration, in g litre^{-1}, of a sodium chloride solution obtained by dissolving 20 g of sodium chloride in water to give 100 cm^3 of solution?

◯ If 20 g are dissolved in water to give 100 cm^3 of solution, then in 1 cm^3, there will be $\frac{20\,g}{100}$ = 0.20 g of sodium chloride. In 1.0 litre there are 1 000 cm^3, thus there would be $1\,000 \times 0.20$ g = 200 g of sodium chloride. So the concentration is 200 g litre^{-1}.

It is usually the case that concentrations of solutions are expressed as the number of *moles* of solute that are dissolved in a specific volume of the solution at a given temperature. Again the volume is usually specified to be one litre. Let's express the concentration of 3.0 g litre^{-1} of sodium chloride dissolved in water in terms of moles per litre, which as a unit we express as mol litre^{-1}.

⬤ What is the molar mass of sodium chloride, NaCl? (The relative atomic masses of sodium and chlorine are 23.0 and 35.5, respectively.)

◯ To obtain the molar mass we add up the relative atomic masses in the formula unit, NaCl, and follow this with the symbol for the gram. This gives (23.0 + 35.5) g, so the molar mass of sodium chloride is 58.5 g.

● How many moles are there in 3.0 g of sodium chloride?

○ 3.0 g of sodium chloride contain $\frac{3.0}{58.5}$ mol, that is 0.051 mol.

● What is the concentration, in mol litre^{-1}, if 3.0 g of sodium chloride are dissolved in one litre of solution?

○ 3.0 g of sodium chloride represent 0.051 mol. This is present in one litre of solution, so the concentration is 0.051 mol litre^{-1}.

● What is the concentration of sodium chloride solution, in mol litre^{-1}, if 30 g of this salt are dissolved in water to give one litre of solution?

○ 30 g of sodium chloride represent $\frac{30}{58.5}$ mol or 0.51 mol. This is present in one litre of solution. Thus the concentration is 0.51 mol litre^{-1}.

● What is the concentration of sodium chloride solution, in mol litre^{-1}, if 20 g are dissolved in water to give 100 cm^3 of solution?

○ In 1 cm^3 of solution there is $\frac{20\,g}{100}$ = 0.20 g of sodium chloride. One litre contains 1 000 cm^3, thus this contains 1 000 $\times$ 0.20 g = 200 g of sodium chloride. This represents $\frac{200}{58.5}$ mol, or 3.4 mol in one litre of solution. Thus the concentration is 3.4 mol litre^{-1}.

In Section 4 we saw that when solid sodium chloride dissolves in water the resulting solution contains equal numbers of sodium ions and chloride ions:

$$NaCl(s) \longrightarrow Na^+(aq) + Cl^-(aq) \tag{7.1}$$

So if one mole of sodium chloride is dissolved in water to form one litre of solution, the solution will contain one mole of Na$^+$(aq) and one mole of Cl$^-$(aq). Thus, a 1.0 mol litre^{-1} solution of sodium chloride will contain 1.0 mol litre^{-1} of Na$^+$(aq) and 1.0 mol litre^{-1} of Cl$^-$(aq).

Things start to get a little tricky when we move on to more complex ionic compounds. For instance, when calcium chloride, $CaCl_2$, dissolves in water the resulting solution contains two chloride ions for every calcium ion:

$$CaCl_2(s) \longrightarrow Ca^{2+}(aq) + 2Cl^-(aq) \tag{7.4}$$

So when we dissolve one mole of calcium chloride in water to form one litre of solution it contains one mole of Ca^{2+}(aq), and *two* moles of Cl$^-$(aq).

● What are the concentrations of Ca^{2+}(aq) and Cl$^-$(aq) in a solution formed by dissolving 3.4 mol of calcium chloride in sufficient water to make one litre of solution?

○ A 3.4 mol litre^{-1} solution of calcium chloride contains 3.4 mol litre^{-1} of Ca^{2+}(aq) and 6.8 mol litre^{-1} of Cl$^-$(aq).

Question 7.2   (a) What is the concentration of Na$^+$(aq), in mol litre^{-1}, if 20 g of sodium chloride are dissolved in water to give one litre of solution? (b) What is the concentration of Cl$^-$(aq), in mol litre^{-1}, if 30 g of calcium chloride are dissolved in water to give one litre of solution? ◀

7.2 The melting and boiling temperatures of water

As you saw in Block 1, life on Earth depends on the presence of water. It is mainly in the liquid form over most of the Earth because the Earth's surface temperature is generally between the normal melting temperature of water, 0 °C, and the normal boiling temperature of water, 100 °C. However, these melting and boiling temperatures, which are so familiar to us, are in fact very remarkable.

Question 7.3   In Block 6 we used the Periodic Table to predict trends in the properties of elements and their compounds. Figure 7.5 shows the boiling temperatures of the covalent dihydrides of the Group VI elements sulfur (S), selenium (Se) and tellurium (Te). The value for the first element (labelled X) in this group is missing. Estimate the boiling temperature you would expect for XH_2 based solely on the trend shown in Figure 7.5. ◀

The first element in Group VI — element X — is oxygen and its dihydride is OH_2, which is an alternative way of writing H_2O — water. We know that the boiling temperature of water is not –70 °C, but +100 °C, a difference of 170 °C! So, what has gone wrong with your prediction from Question 7.3?

⬤ Briefly describe what happens at the molecular level when water evaporates to give water vapour.

◯ The process of evaporation involves a change from a state where the water molecules are relatively close together in the liquid, to one in which they are farther apart, essentially independent of one another, in the vapour. Energy is needed to overcome the attractive interactions between the molecules in the liquid and to release them into the vapour phase. Evaporation is an endothermic process.

⬤ For any liquid, how do you think the magnitude of the attractive interactions between the molecules in the liquid will affect the boiling temperature?

◯ As the temperature of a liquid rises, the molecules gain kinetic energy. Eventually they have sufficient energy to overcome the attractive interactions and leave the liquid. The stronger the attractive interactions the more energy the molecules will need to achieve this. Thus, the stronger the attractive interactions, the higher the boiling temperature.

You may recall that the particle model developed in Block 2 required attractive interactions between molecules both in the liquid and in the solid state. But what are these attractive interactions?

7.2.1 Intermolecular interactions

In Section 4 you met ionic compounds, which are made up of positive and negative ions. Oppositely charged ions are attracted to each other by electrical interactions. Thus an ionic solid consists of a regular arrangement of positively and negatively charged ions. In the same section, you also considered molecular substances such as iodine, in which neutral I_2 molecules form regular arrays in the solid state. You saw in Figure 4.5 that the two atoms in each I_2 molecule are held together by a covalent bond. But what about the interactions between individual I_2 molecules that hold the solid together?

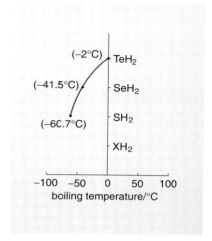

Figure 7.5   The boiling temperatures of the covalent dihydrides of the Group VI elements.

Even though molecules are electrically neutral because they carry equal amounts of positive and negative charges, they can still be attracted to one another via **intermolecular interactions**. We shall deal with two types: London interactions and hydrogen bonding.

London interactions

Figure 7.5 showed that the boiling temperatures of the covalent dihydrides of the Group VI elements sulfur (S), selenium (Se) and tellurium (Te) increased steadily as we went down the group. This is a result of **London interactions**, named after the German-born physicist Fritz London (1900–1954) who first explained them. These interactions, *which occur between all atoms and molecules*, whether they are charged or not, result from subtle fluctuations in the way that electrons are distributed in a molecule. These fluctuations influence the electron distributions in neighbouring molecules and, although we shall not go into further detail, give rise to attractive interactions that are electrical in nature. The strength of London interactions depends, amongst other factors, on relative molecular mass: the larger the relative molecular mass of a molecule the larger the attractive interaction. Thus the boiling temperatures of H_2S (relative molecular mass 34.0), H_2Se (relative molecular mass 81.0) and H_2Te (relative molecular mass 130) rise steadily as the relative molecular masses, and hence the London interactions, increase down the group. However, although London interactions between molecules can be reasonably large, they are nowhere near as strong as the interaction between two atoms joined by a covalent bond.

Question 7.4   (a) What are the relative molecular masses of fluorine (F_2), chlorine (Cl_2), bromine (Br_2) and iodine (I_2)? (b) Assuming that the most significant intermolecular interactions are London interactions, what trend would you predict in the boiling temperatures of fluorine, chlorine, bromine and iodine? ◄

Hydrogen bonding

The prediction made in Question 7.3 for the boiling temperature of water assumed that the same type of attractive interaction operated between all the molecules in the series of dihydrides. For water to have a boiling temperature so much higher than predicted there must be an additional type of intermolecular interaction present in liquid water.

This additional interaction is extremely important and is called hydrogen bonding. A **hydrogen bond** is a particularly strong type of intermolecular interaction, which occurs when a hydrogen atom is covalently bonded to one strongly electronegative atom but is also close to a strongly electronegative atom in another molecule. This is shown in Figure 7.6a.

As you saw in Figure 7.2, the atoms in a water molecule carry partial charges; a small positive charge on both hydrogen atoms and a small negative charge on the oxygen atom. When two water molecules are adjacent to one another, there will be an electrical interaction between the small positive charge on the hydrogen atom of one molecule and the small negative charge on the oxygen atom of another. This results in the formation of a hydrogen bond as shown in Figure 7.6b. The situation in liquid water itself is shown schematically in Figure 7.6c.

Hydrogen is unique in being able to form this type of bond because it is such a small atom. For this reason the strongly electronegative atom Y in Figure 7.6a can come close enough to interact with the positive charge carried by the hydrogen atom.

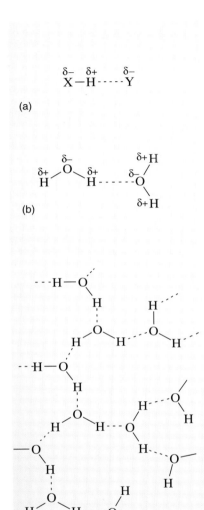

Figure 7.6 (a) A hydrogen atom between two strongly electronegative atoms, X and Y. A solid line between atoms represents a covalent bond and a dashed line represents a hydrogen bond. (b) The formation of a hydrogen bond between two water molecules. (c) The network of hydrogen bonds between water molecules in liquid water.

Important examples of hydrogen bonds between strongly electronegative atoms are shown in Figure 7.7. Although these hydrogen bonds are stronger than other intermolecular interactions, you should remember that they are still much weaker than covalent or ionic bonds.

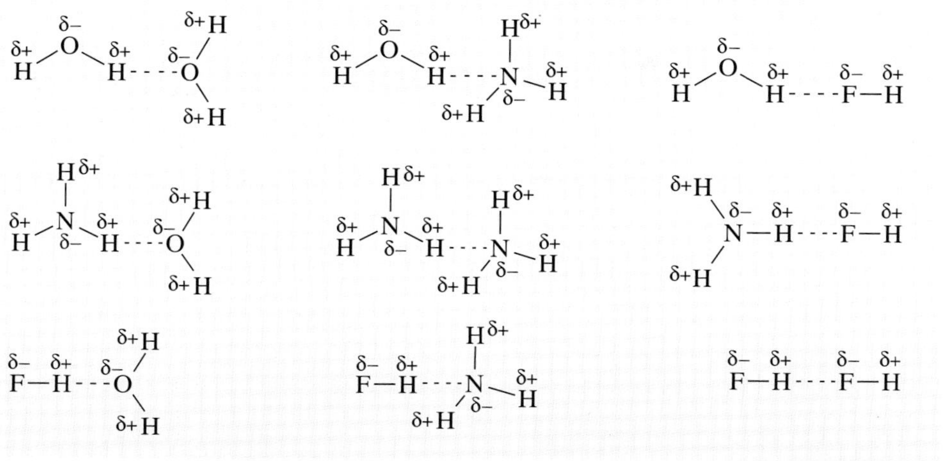

Figure 7.7   Important examples of hydrogen bonds. Hydrogen bonds only link hydrogen with three of the most electronegative elements, fluorine, oxygen and nitrogen.

In Question 7.3, you saw that the boiling temperature of water would be about $-70\,°C$ if London interactions only were involved. However, water molecules have an additional attractive interaction between them — hydrogen bonding. This means that the water molecules are held together more strongly than would be expected on the basis of London interactions alone and, as a consequence, the melting and boiling temperatures of water are increased. Hydrogen bonding not only accounts for water being a liquid at room temperature but, as you will see later, it plays a key role in the DNA molecules that carry the genetic code and in the way that pharmaceuticals work.

Question 7.5   For each of the following pairs of compounds, predict which one has the higher boiling temperature.

(a) Methane, CH_4, or ethane, C_2H_6. (Assume that London interactions are the only intermolecular interactions between methane molecules or ethane molecules in the liquid state.)

(b) Hydrogen, H_2, or hydrogen fluoride, HF. (Assume that London interactions are the only intermolecular interactions between hydrogen molecules in the liquid state.) ◀

Question 7.6   Table 7.1, in the answer to Question 7.4, lists the melting temperatures of fluorine (F_2), chlorine (Cl_2), bromine (Br_2) and iodine (I_2). How would you account for the trend in the melting temperatures? ◀

Question 7.7   How would you expect the melting temperatures of the Group V trihydrides (NH_3, PH_3, AsH_3, SbH_3 and BiH_3) to change down the group? ◀

7.3 Acidic solutions

Another important property of water is its ability to reveal the acidic behaviour of certain chemical compounds.

- Make a list of the points you remember about acids from Block 6.

- In Block 6 (Sections 2, 11 and 13), you learnt that an acid does the following: dissolves in water and the solution turns blue litmus red; reacts with metals, such as magnesium and zinc, with liberation of hydrogen; reacts with calcium carbonate to give carbon dioxide; forms salts when the hydrogen atoms of an acid are replaced by metal atoms; is neutralized by basic hydroxides to form salts (during neutralization, the hydrogen atoms of the acid and the hydroxide groups of the basic hydroxide combine to form water); contains hydrogen and yields hydrogen ions, $H^+(aq)$, when it dissolves in water.

Notice in particular that an acid yields hydrogen ions *when it dissolves in water*. For example, the three common acids that you met in Block 6 were hydrochloric acid, nitric acid and sulfuric acid. They dissolve in water, and then break down as follows:

$$HCl(aq) \longrightarrow H^+(aq) + Cl^-(aq) \tag{7.5}$$

$$HNO_3(aq) \longrightarrow H^+(aq) + NO_3^-(aq) \tag{7.6}$$

$$H_2SO_4(aq) \longrightarrow 2H^+(aq) + SO_4^{2-}(aq) \tag{7.7}$$

Each of these equations represents a dissociation, because they each involve the breakdown of an acid into hydrogen ions and the corresponding negative ions. The key role that water plays in this process is to stabilize the positive and negative ions, as we saw in Figure 7.3.

As well as the acids mentioned above, you may have come across other acids, such as acetic acid, which is a component of vinegar, and citric acid, which is found in lemons. Such acids are mild enough to be used on food, whereas the sulfuric acid used in car batteries most certainly cannot be drunk, and has to be handled with care as it can burn skin and damage clothing. As you will see, the difference between these solutions is mainly due to differences in their hydrogen ion concentrations.

7.3.1 Hydrogen ion concentration

Activity 7.1   Measuring the hydrogen ion concentration of household solutions

In this activity, you will measure the hydrogen ion concentrations of different household solutions and thus find out how these values relate to intuitive ideas of solutions being more or less acid. ◀

Activity 7.1 demonstrated that the hydrogen ion concentration can be related to the acidity of a solution.

- What is the hydrogen ion concentration, in mol litre^{-1}, if 20.0 g of hydrogen chloride are dissolved in water to give one litre of solution?

- The formula unit of hydrogen chloride is HCl. The molar mass of hydrogen chloride is thus $(1.01 + 35.5)$ g, or 36.5 g.

  20.0 g of hydrogen chloride are $\frac{20.0}{36.5}$ mol, that is 0.548 mol.

This amount is contained in one litre of solution, so the concentration of hydrogen chloride is 0.548 mol litre^{-1}. According to Equation 7.5, hydrogen chloride dissolves in water to give one hydrogen ion and one chloride ion for every formula unit of dissolved hydrogen chloride, and so the hydrogen ion concentration is 0.548 mol litre^{-1}.

Vinegar contains acetic acid. You will learn more about the structure of this acid in Section 14, but for now we will keep things simple and refer to a molecule of acetic acid as HAc, where the H refers to the hydrogen that forms H$^+$(aq) when the acid dissolves in water, and Ac is shorthand for acetate — the rest of the molecule. (Note that Ac is *not* a single element.) Thus, acetic acid dissociates in water to give hydrogen ions and acetate ions, Ac$^-$(aq):

$$HAc(aq) \longrightarrow H^+(aq) + Ac^-(aq) \tag{7.8}$$

If we were to test the conductivity of vinegar, using the apparatus described in Block 6, Section 13.2 and Figure 4.1 of this block, we would find that the light would not come on. What does this tell us about the concentration of the ions in this solution?

Clearly, vinegar is not a good electrical conductor. Therefore, the concentration of the ions in vinegar must be very low.

This conclusion is consistent with the measurement you may have made of the hydrogen ion concentration in vinegar in Activity 7.1. You should have found a value in the range from 1×10^{-2} to 1×10^{-3} mol litre^{-1}. This value is *considerably less* than might have been expected, because vinegar has a composition that is roughly equivalent to dissolving two moles of acetic acid in sufficient water to make up one litre of solution. If this acetic acid dissociated completely, then the hydrogen ion concentration would be about 2 mol litre^{-1}.

When hydrogen chloride dissolves in water, effectively all the HCl molecules dissociate to give H$^+$(aq) and Cl$^-$(aq) ions. However, when acetic acid dissolves in water only a *small fraction* of the acetic acid molecules dissociate to give hydrogen ions and acetate ions. For example, if 1.000 mol of acetic acid is dissolved in sufficient water to give one litre of solution we end up with 0.996 mol of acetic acid molecules and only 0.004 mol of H$^+$(aq) and 0.004 mol of Ac$^-$(aq) in this volume. *The solute consists mainly of undissociated acetic acid molecules.*

The dissociation of acetic acid in water is another example of a reaction that goes so far and then no further; it reaches chemical equilibrium. The equilibrium state is dynamic; acetic acid molecules are continuously breaking down into hydrogen ions and acetate ions and this is balanced by the reverse reaction — hydrogen ions and acetate ions recombining to give acetic acid molecules. To highlight the equilibrium it is best written as:

$$HAc(aq) \rightleftharpoons H^+(aq) + Ac^-(aq) \tag{7.9}$$

where the symbol $\rightleftharpoons$ indicates that the reaction takes place in both directions. Acids, such as hydrogen chloride, that dissolve in water and effectively dissociate completely to give hydrogen ions, H$^+$(aq), and the corresponding negatively charged ions are known as **strong acids**. Acids, such as acetic acid, that dissolve in water and are only *partially* dissociated are called **weak acids**.

It is important to distinguish between the *strength* of an acid and the *concentration* of an acid. A solution is said to be concentrated if the concentration of the solute in the solution is high. The concept of strength, however, simply refers to the extent to which an acid is dissociated in solution; strong acids lie at one end of the scale because they are completely dissociated. Acids that do not satisfy this criterion are designated as weak. When talking about the concentration of acid solutions, it is a good idea to refer to 'dilute' or 'concentrated' solutions, rather than 'weak' or 'strong' solutions. For example, it is possible to have a concentrated solution of a weak acid.

Before we can develop ideas on acidity further you need to have a better understanding of chemical equilibrium, and how equilibria respond to external influences. We will therefore introduce some important aspects of equilibrium in Section 8, before returning to the subject of acids in Section 9.

Question 7.8   (a) Sulfuric acid is a strong acid. What is the hydrogen ion concentration of a 0.1 mol litre^{-1} solution of sulfuric acid?

(b) Hydrogen cyanide, HCN, is used in the manufacture of nylon. It is a weak acid:

$$HCN(aq) \rightleftharpoons H^+(aq) + CN^-(aq)$$

What can you say about the hydrogen ion concentration of a 1.0 mol litre^{-1} solution of hydrogen cyanide? ◄

7.4   Summary of Section 7

1   A solute dissolves in a solvent to give a solution. The concentration of a solution at a particular temperature is expressed as the amount of solute in a specific volume of solution, and common units are g litre^{-1} and mol litre^{-1}.

2   Solubility describes the maximum amount of a solute that will dissolve in a given amount of solvent, usually 100 g for water, at a particular temperature.

3   A saturated solution is in a steady state. Such an equilibrium state is dynamic; the rate at which material dissolves in the solvent is matched by the rate at which dissolved material returns to the solid state.

4   The molecules in solids and liquids are attracted to each other by intermolecular interactions. The strength of these interactions affects melting temperatures and boiling temperatures.

5   All molecules are attracted to one another via London interactions, and the strength of the attraction increases with relative molecular mass.

6   Hydrogen bonding occurs when a hydrogen atom is bonded to one strongly electronegative atom and is close to a strongly electronegative atom in another molecule.

7   Acids yield hydrogen ions when they dissolve in water. Acidity depends on the hydrogen ion concentration. When strong acids dissolve they dissociate completely to give hydrogen ions and their corresponding negatively charged ions. Weak acids only *partially* dissociate in water.

Chemical equilibrium

8

In the previous section, in the discussion both of saturated solutions and of the dissociation of acetic acid in water, the idea was introduced that chemical equilibrium represents a state of *dynamic balance*. In general, for a chemical reaction that proceeds to equilibrium we can write

$$\text{reactants} \rightleftharpoons \text{products} \tag{8.1}$$

At equilibrium the forward reaction (left to right) and the reverse reaction (right to left) occur at the same rate and, consequently, there is *no further change* in the relative amounts of products and reactants present in the reaction mixture. For a reaction proceeding to equilibrium, therefore, the 'end' of reaction is when the composition of the reaction mixture no longer changes with time — no matter how long the wait. It is important to emphasize that reactants and products co-exist in a reaction mixture at equilibrium (Figure 8.1).

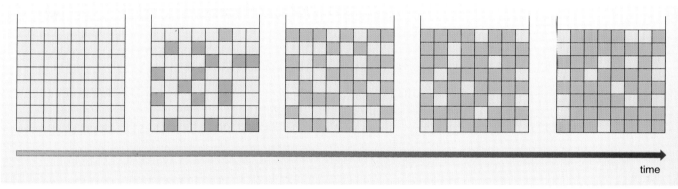

time

Figure 8.1 A simple pictorial representation of a chemical reaction going to equilibrium. At the start of reaction only reactant molecules, represented by green squares, are present. As the reaction proceeds, product molecules are formed. These are represented by orange squares. Eventually, in the fourth frame, equilibrium is reached. The relative proportion of products and reactants then no longer changes with time — as can be verified in the final frame. The change in distribution of the green and orange squares between the fourth and the final frame indicates that there is a state of dynamic balance at equilibrium. In this state reactants are continuously being converted into products, and products are continuously being converted into reactants.

For some reactions, the composition of the equilibrium mixture is such that the relative proportion of the products far exceeds that of the reactants. These reactions, for all practical purposes, can be described as going to *completion* since, in effect, all of the reactants are consumed. A few examples of reactions that behave in this way were shown in the video sequence for Activity 6.1.

The video also illustrated an important property of reaction mixtures at equilibrium. You saw that the relative proportions of reactants and products in an equilibrium mixture can change with a change in conditions. One of the examples, illustrating the effect of a change in temperature, is reproduced in Figure 8.2.

Figure 8.2 The effect of a change of temperature on the composition of an equilibrium mixture. The red colour of the solution indicates that the reactant is dominant. On raising the temperature, the solution turns blue, indicating that the product is dominant.

In this section we look at chemical equilibrium in more detail, both for reactions that involve only gases and for those that occur in solution. In particular we focus on predicting the changes that occur in an equilibrium mixture as a result of changing specific conditions, such as the pressure, temperature or concentration. We begin with a CD-ROM activity.

Activity 8.1 Chemical equilibrium: Part I

This CD-ROM activity starts with an introduction to chemical equilibrium. You will then investigate how a change in pressure or temperature can affect the relative proportions of reactants and products in a reaction mixture at equilibrium. ◀

8.1 Le Chatelier's principle

The important idea about chemical equilibrium is that it represents a state of dynamic balance: reactants are continuously being converted into products, and vice versa. At equilibrium, the relative proportions of reactants and products in a reaction mixture remain fixed, provided that there is no change in any of the reaction conditions. However, if a particular reaction condition (or constraint), such as pressure or temperature, is changed, then there is a change in the overall composition of the equilibrium mixture. As you saw in Activity 8.1, it is possible to *predict qualitatively* the way in which an equilibrium mixture will respond to a change in conditions.

The basis for making predictions is summarized by **Le Chatelier's principle**, which has the general form:

> When a system in equilibrium is subject to an external constraint, the system responds in a way that tends to oppose the effect of the constraint.

In the following sections we shall look at further examples of reactions that proceed to equilibrium and, in so doing, we shall review and consolidate the conclusions reached in Activity 8.1.

8.2 Gaseous reactions

A variety of chemical reactions, including some of considerable industrial importance, involve reactants and products that are gases. For this type of reaction, the relative proportions of reactants and products in the equilibrium mixture can depend on both pressure and temperature. The effects of changes in these two conditions are independent of one another and are treated separately in the following sections.

8.2.1 The effect of a change in pressure

In Section 7.3 of Block 6, you explored the changes in the pressure of a gas trapped in the sealed end of a U-tube containing mercury (Figure 8.3). Adding more mercury to the open arm of the U-tube increases the pressure of the trapped gas.

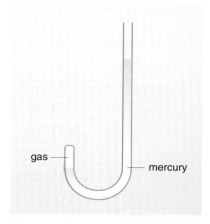

Figure 8.3   A U-tube in which gas is trapped in the sealed end by mercury.

Suppose a reaction, in which both the reactants and the products are gases, takes place and reaches equilibrium in the sealed end of the U-tube. We can use Le Chatelier's principle to predict how the composition of this equilibrium mixture will change if the pressure in the sealed end is increased by adding more mercury to the U-tube. The external constraint in this case is an increase in pressure. To minimize the effect of this constraint, the composition of the equilibrium mixture will change in a way that tends to reduce the pressure. We can see more clearly what this means if we also recall from Block 6 that pressure depends on the number of particles hitting the walls of the containing vessel. So, we would predict that, to reduce the pressure, the composition of the equilibrium mixture will shift in a direction that corresponds, if possible, to a reduction in the number of molecules in the gas phase. This direction can be determined from the chemical equation. A few examples, including those you have already encountered in Activity 8.1, will show these ideas in action.

Sulfuric acid is a major product of the chemical industry. One stage in the most common method of production involves the reaction of sulfur dioxide, SO_2, with oxygen to give sulfur trioxide, SO_3. The chemical equation for this reaction is:

$$2SO_2(g) + O_2(g) \rightleftharpoons 2SO_3(g) \tag{8.2}$$

Le Chatelier's principle can be used to predict how the proportion of sulfur trioxide present at equilibrium, that is the **equilibrium yield** of this substance, varies with pressure. Let us consider the effect of increasing the pressure of the equilibrium mixture. To respond to this increase in pressure the composition of the equilibrium mixture will shift in a direction that results in a reduction in the number of molecules in the gas phase. According to the balanced chemical equation there are two moles of sulfur dioxide molecules and one mole of oxygen molecules, giving a total of three moles of reactant molecules. There are only two moles of product molecules. Thus an increase in pressure will favour the formation of the product sulfur trioxide and there will be a larger proportion of this substance in the equilibrium mixture. In other words, the equilibrium yield of sulfur trioxide will increase with increasing pressure.

As a second example, consider the production of hydrogen gas from natural gas and steam, which is used as a source of hydrogen in industrial processes. Natural gas is mostly methane, CH_4, and so the chemical reaction that takes place can be written as:

$$CH_4(g) + H_2O(g) \rightleftharpoons CO(g) + 3H_2(g) \tag{8.3}$$

● For this balanced chemical equation, which direction corresponds to a reduction in the number of gas-phase molecules?

○ There are two moles of reactant molecules (one of methane and one of water) and four moles of product molecules (one of carbon monoxide and three of hydrogen). The direction right to left, that is the reverse reaction as written, · corresponds to a reduction in the number of gas-phase molecules.

An increase in pressure, therefore, will result in a decrease in the proportion of hydrogen gas in the equilibrium mixture. Thus, in the absence of any other considerations, to increase the equilibrium yield of hydrogen gas it would be necessary to operate the process at a lower pressure.

Finally, we look at the reaction between nitrogen and oxygen to give nitrogen monoxide, NO:

$$N_2(g) + O_2(g) \rightleftharpoons 2NO(g) \tag{8.4}$$

This reaction takes place in the atmosphere during thunderstorms and also during the combustion process in car engines.

● What would be the effect on the equilibrium mixture if this reaction occurred at a higher pressure?

○ There are two moles of reactant molecules and the same number of moles of product molecules, and so increasing the pressure will have no effect on the composition of the equilibrium mixture.

The flow diagram in Figure 8.4 contains a summary of the effect of pressure changes on an equilibrium mixture involving gases only.

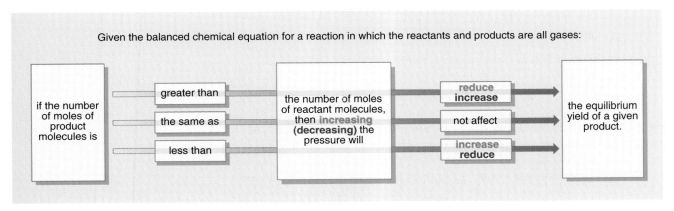

Given the balanced chemical equation for a reaction in which the reactants and products are all gases:

if the number of moles of product molecules is — greater than / the same as / less than — the number of moles of reactant molecules, then **increasing** (**decreasing**) the pressure will — reduce **increase** / not affect / **increase** reduce — the equilibrium yield of a given product.

Figure 8.4 A flow diagram summarizing the effect of pressure changes on an equilibrium mixture involving gases only.

Question 8.1 Hydrogen cyanide, HCN, can be prepared from methane and ammonia. The reaction is represented by the following chemical equation:

$$CH_4(g) + NH_3(g) \rightleftharpoons HCN(g) + 3H_2(g) \tag{8.5}$$

At normal temperatures and pressures, the equilibrium yield of hydrogen cyanide is too low for the reaction to be useful. Would operating the reaction at an increased pressure improve the equilibrium yield? ◀

8.2.2 The effect of a change in temperature

A change in temperature can also have a significant effect on the composition of an equilibrium mixture. Once again, Le Chatelier's principle can be used to predict the effect, which depends on whether the reaction is exothermic or endothermic.

● What are the respective characteristics of an exothermic reaction and an endothermic reaction?

○ These were discussed in Section 6. An exothermic reaction is one that releases energy in the form of heat to its surroundings. An endothermic reaction is one that absorbs energy in the form of heat from its surroundings.

The thermochemical nature of the forward and reverse directions of a reaction that proceeds to equilibrium can be considered separately. Thus if the reaction is exothermic in the forward direction, then it will be endothermic in the reverse direction, and vice versa.

If the temperature of a reaction mixture at equilibrium is raised, then Le Chatelier's principle predicts that the equilibrium mixture will change its composition so as to favour the direction of reaction that is endothermic. This is because, in this direction, energy in the form of heat is absorbed, and this tends to minimize the effect of raising the temperature. Similarly, if the temperature of a reaction mixture at equilibrium is lowered then the equilibrium mixture will change its composition so as to favour the direction of reaction that is exothermic.

● Why is this?

○ An exothermic reaction releases energy in the form of heat, and this will tend to minimize the effect of lowering the temperature.

We shall now consider how the reactions we looked at in Section 8.2.1 respond to changes in temperature.

The formation of hydrogen from methane and steam is represented by the thermochemical equation:

$$CH_4(g) + H_2O(g) \rightleftharpoons CO(g) + 3H_2(g) \quad \Delta H = +206 \text{ kJ} \tag{8.6}$$

Note that the enthalpy change, ΔH, refers *only* to the the forward direction of the reaction. This statement applies to *all* of the thermochemical equations we consider in this block. The forward direction of the reaction in Equation 8.6 is endothermic, and so an increase in temperature will result in a higher equilibrium yield of hydrogen gas.

The thermochemical equation for the formation of sulfur trioxide is

$$2SO_2(g) + O_2(g) \rightleftharpoons 2SO_3(g) \quad \Delta H = -198 \text{ kJ} \tag{8.7}$$

● For the production of sulfur trioxide, would operating the reaction at a higher temperature increase the equilibrium yield of this product?

○ The forward reaction is exothermic. Thus a rise in temperature will *not* favour an increase in the equilibrium yield of sulfur trioxide.

Operating the reaction in Equation 8.7 at a higher temperature will result in the composition of the equilibrium mixture changing so that the relative proportion of the reactants is increased. That is, the reverse direction of the reaction, which is endothermic, is favoured.

Question 8.2 The thermochemical equation for the reaction between nitrogen and oxygen to form nitrogen monoxide is:

$$N_2(g) + O_2(g) \rightleftharpoons 2NO(g) \quad \Delta H = +181 \text{ kJ} \tag{8.8}$$

Will the equilibrium yield of nitrogen monoxide at 500 °C be greater or less than that at room temperature? ◄

A flow diagram that summarizes the discussion in this section is given in Figure 8.5.

Figure 8.5 A flow diagram summarizing the effect of temperature changes on an equilibrium mixture involving gases only.

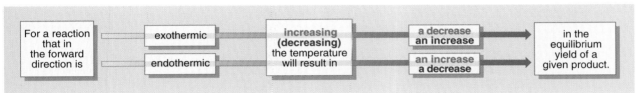

8.3 Chemical equilibrium in solution

We now turn our attention to reactions that occur in solution.

Activity 8.1 Chemical equilibrium: Part II

In this activity you will investigate how a change in concentration affects the relative proportions of reactants and products in a reaction mixture at equilibrium. ◄

As an example of how a change in the concentration of a reactant or a product affects the equilibrium yield, we shall consider the dissociation of acetic acid in water. You saw in Section 7 that acetic acid is a weak acid and that the chemical equation for the dissociation reaction at equilibrium can be written as:

$$HAc(aq) \rightleftharpoons H^+(aq) + Ac^-(aq) \tag{7.9}$$

As you discovered in Activity 8.1, altering the concentration of a particular substance in an equilibrium mixture at constant temperature results in the concentrations of other substances, in the mixture also changing. Thus, for example, we could imagine adding 'acetate ions' to an equilibrium mixture of acetic acid in water. This could be achieved by adding a salt, such as sodium acetate, NaAc, which dissolves fully in water:

$$NaAc(s) \longrightarrow Na^+(aq) + Ac^-(aq) \tag{8.9}$$

⬤ According to Le Chatelier's principle, what changes would you expect to occur?

◯ Adding sodium acetate increases the concentration of $Ac^-(aq)$. Thus, according to Le Chatelier's principle, the equilibrium represented by Equation 7.9 responds by trying to minimize this increase in concentration of $Ac^-(aq)$. This is achieved by the reverse direction of the reaction producing more HAc(aq). Thus the composition of the equilibrium mixture shifts so that there is an increase in the proportion of HAc(aq) and a decrease in the proportions of $H^+(aq)$ and $Ac^-(aq)$.

Note that the sodium ions formed by the dissolution of sodium acetate in water, Equation 8.9, have no effect on the equilibrium and simply act as 'spectators'.

Le Chatelier's principle is useful for making qualitative predictions, but to move towards a more *quantitative* understanding of equilibrium we need to introduce the concept of an equilibrium constant, K, for a given reaction. The first demonstration of this concept predated Le Chatelier's work by more than 20 years. In 1864 Cato Guldberg and his brother-in-law Peter Waage, who worked together in Christiana (now Oslo), noticed that the molar concentrations of the products and reactants in an equilibrium mixture for a particular reaction always satisfy a certain relationship. You explored this relationship for reactions in solution in Activity 8.1, and it also holds for the reactions of gases.

8.3.1   The equilibrium constant, K

One of the reactions that you may have considered in Activity 8.1 was the dissociation of acetic acid in water (Equation 7.9). Figure 8.6 illustrates the relationship between the concentrations of HAc(aq), H^+(aq) and Ac^-(aq) *in equilibrium mixtures* formed, for example, by adding different amounts of sodium acetate to the original solution at 25 °C.

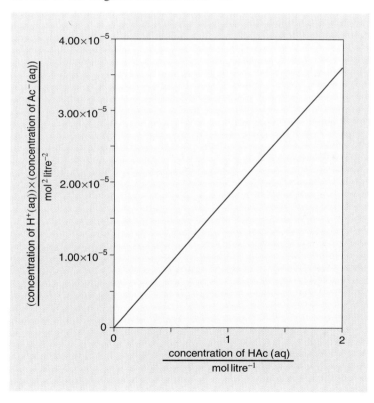

Figure 8.6
A graph illustrating the form of the equilibrium relationship for the dissociation of acetic acid in water at 25 °C. The concentrations are equilibrium molar concentrations.

In the graph in Figure 8.6, the equilibrium molar concentration of HAc(aq) is plotted along the horizontal axis. The equilibrium molar concentration of H^+(aq) multiplied by the equilibrium molar concentration of Ac^-(aq) is plotted along the vertical axis. The graph is a straight line, indicating that there is a proportionality relationship:

$$\left(\begin{array}{c}\text{equilibrium molar}\\\text{concentration of }H^+(aq)\end{array}\right) \times \left(\begin{array}{c}\text{equilibrium molar}\\\text{concentration of }Ac^-(aq)\end{array}\right) \propto \left(\begin{array}{c}\text{equilibrium molar}\\\text{concentration of }HAc(aq)\end{array}\right) \qquad (8.10)$$

65

As written above, this relationship is quite cumbersome, so a special notation is used for molar concentration: the chemical formula of the ion, or molecule, is enclosed in square brackets. For example, the molar concentration of $H^+(aq)$ in any solution would be represented by $[H^+(aq)]$ and, typically, be measured in mol litre^{-1}. The equilibrium relationship now becomes:

$$[H^+(aq)] \times [Ac^-(aq)] \propto [HAc(aq)] \tag{8.11}$$

You saw in Block 5 that a proportionality relationship can be turned into an equation by introducing a constant of proportionality. In this case the constant of proportionality is known as the **equilibrium constant** K for the dissociation of acetic acid in water, that is:

$$[H^+(aq)] \times [Ac^-(aq)] = K[HAc(aq)] \tag{8.12}$$

It is usual to rearrange Equation 8.12 so that all of the concentration terms are on one side of the equation, that is:

$$K = \frac{\left[H^+(aq)\right]\left[Ac^-(aq)\right]}{\left[HAc(aq)\right]} \tag{8.13}$$

It is very important to remember that each of the molar concentration terms in this relationship refers to the situation in the *equilibrium* mixture.

○ What is the appropriate unit for the equilibrium constant for the dissociation of acetic acid in water, given that the equilibrium concentrations are measured in mol litre^{-1}?

○ As always, the units on both sides of an equation must balance. So:

$$\text{unit of } K = \text{unit of } \frac{\left[H^+(aq)\right]\left[Ac^-(aq)\right]}{\left[HAc(aq)\right]}$$

$$= \frac{(\text{mol litre}^{-1})(\text{mol litre}^{-1})}{\text{mol litre}^{-1}}$$

$$= \text{mol litre}^{-1}$$

The value of the equilibrium constant depends only on temperature. So, *at a given temperature* the magnitude of K is *fixed*. In other words, no matter what the initial composition of a reaction mixture involving acetic acid in water at a given temperature, the value of K determined from the equilibrium concentrations of $HAc(aq)$, $H^+(aq)$ and $Ac^-(aq)$ will always be the same.

The equilibrium relationship in Equation 8.13 can be modified so that it applies to *any* acid HX that dissociates in water to give $H^+(aq)$ and an ion with a single negative charge, $X^-(aq)$. The chemical equation for the dissociation is:

$$HX(aq) \rightleftharpoons H^+(aq) + X^-(aq) \tag{8.14}$$

and the equilibrium relationship is:

$$K = \frac{\left[H^+(aq)\right]\left[X^-(aq)\right]}{\left[HX(aq)\right]} \tag{8.15}$$

The values of K at a given temperature are different for different acids.

Question 8.3   Nitrous acid dissociates in water according to the equation:

$$HNO_2(aq) \rightleftharpoons H^+(aq) + NO_2^-(aq) \tag{8.16}$$

where $NO_2^-(aq)$ is the nitrite ion. Table 8.1 provides information about three solutions of this acid in water at 25 °C. Use this information to calculate the equilibrium constant for the dissociation reaction at 25 °C and also to demonstrate that the magnitude of this quantity has a fixed value. ◄

Table 8.1   Equilibrium molar concentrations in three solutions of nitrous acid in water at 25 °C.

Solution	$\dfrac{\left[HNO_2(aq)\right]}{mol\ litre^{-1}}$	$\dfrac{\left[H^+(aq)\right]}{mol\ litre^{-1}}$	$\dfrac{\left[NO_2^-(aq)\right]}{mol\ litre^{-1}}$
A	0.090	6.2×10^{-3}	6.2×10^{-3}
B	0.20	9.3×10^{-3}	9.3×10^{-3}
C	0.30	11.4×10^{-3}	11.4×10^{-3}

8.3.2   The magnitude of the equilibrium constant

The value of the equilibrium constant for the dissociation of acetic acid in water at 25 °C is $K = 1.8 \times 10^{-5}\ mol\ litre^{-1}$. The magnitude of this quantity provides direct information on the extent to which acetic acid dissociates in pure water; that is, how far the reaction proceeds before equilibrium is reached. We will show why this is the case and, in the process, illustrate a particular method of calculation.

Suppose that sufficient acetic acid is dissolved in water at 25 °C so that, at equilibrium, the concentration of *undissociated* acetic acid, [HAc(aq)], is 1.0 mol litre^{-1}. Given this information, we can substitute the values $K = 1.8 \times 10^{-5}\ mol\ litre^{-1}$ and [HAc(aq)] = 1.0 mol litre^{-1} into Equation 8.13, so that:

$$1.8 \times 10^{-5}\ mol\ litre^{-1} = \frac{\left[H^+(aq)\right]\left[Ac^-(aq)\right]}{1.0\ mol\ litre^{-1}} \tag{8.17}$$

This equation can be simplified by multiplying both sides by '1.0 mol litre^{-1}' to give:

$$(1.8 \times 10^{-5}\ mol\ litre^{-1}) \times (1.0\ mol\ litre^{-1}) = \left[H^+(aq)\right]\left[Ac^-(aq)\right] \tag{8.18}$$

which is equivalent to:

$$\left[H^+(aq)\right]\left[Ac^-(aq)\right] = 1.8 \times 10^{-5}\ mol^2\ litre^{-2} \tag{8.19}$$

Now remember that for every acetic acid molecule that dissociates in water, one $H^+(aq)$ ion and one $Ac^-(aq)$ ion enter into solution. This means that the numbers of these two kinds of ion, and hence their concentrations, must be equal; so at equilibrium [H$^+$(aq)] = [Ac$^-$(aq)]. We are now in a position to calculate, say, the concentration of acetate ions in the equilibrium mixture. To do this we substitute [Ac$^-$(aq)] for [H$^+$(aq)] in Equation 8.19, with the result that:

$$\left[Ac^-(aq)\right]\left[Ac^-(aq)\right] = 1.8 \times 10^{-5}\ mol^2\ litre^{-2} \tag{8.20}$$

and then take the square root of both sides of this equation:

$$\left[\text{Ac}^-(\text{aq})\right] = \sqrt{1.8 \times 10^{-5}\,\text{mol}^2\,\text{litre}^{-2}}$$

$$\left[\text{Ac}^-(\text{aq})\right] = 4.2 \times 10^{-3}\,\text{mol}\,\text{litre}^{-1} \tag{8.21}$$

Note that this equilibrium concentration of acetate ions is considerably less than that of the undissociated acetic acid [HAc(aq)], which is 1.0 mol litre^{-1} in this case. This means that dissociation does not proceed very far before equilibrium is reached. This can be expressed by saying that the *equilibrium position*, which reflects the composition of the equilibrium mixture, lies well over to the left of Equation 7.9.

○ Is the calculation we have just carried out consistent with the view that acetic acid is a weak acid at 25 °C?

○ Yes, in Section 7 a weak acid was defined as an acid that partially dissociates in water.

Activity 8.2   Solving problems in chemistry

In this activity you will use the strategy for solving problems that you developed in Block 5 to tackle a problem that involves an equlibrium reaction. ◄

Our discussion in this section illustrates that the magnitude of an equilibrium constant indicates how far a reaction will proceed before equilibrium is reached. If the magnitude is very small, as for the dissociation of acetic acid in water (1.8 × 10^{-5} mol litre^{-1}), then hardly any reaction occurs at all. As the magnitude increases, for example as in the case of the dissociation of iodic acid in water (0.17 mol litre^{-1}), then the reaction will proceed further before equilibrium is reached. In the case of the dissociation of a strong acid in water, then the magnitude of the equilibrium constant is extremely large since effectively the reaction goes to completion.

8.3.3   The response to change: the equilibrium relationship

Changing the concentration of a particular substance in an equilibrium mixture (at constant temperature) will result in a change in the overall composition of the mixture. The nature of the change can be predicted using Le Chatelier's principle. An alternative, and useful, approach is to consider what happens in terms of the expression for the equilibrium constant.

If we once again consider the dissociation of acetic acid in water:

$$\text{HAc(aq)} \rightleftharpoons \text{H}^+(\text{aq}) + \text{Ac}^-(\text{aq}) \tag{7.9}$$

then the equilibrium relationship is:

$$K = \frac{\left[\text{H}^+(\text{aq})\right]\left[\text{Ac}^-(\text{aq})\right]}{\left[\text{HAc(aq)}\right]} \tag{8.13}$$

The equilibrium mixture can be disturbed by adding acetate ions. This can be achieved, as we have indicated previously, by adding sodium acetate to the mixture (Equation 8.9).

The *immediate* result of adding acetate ions is to disturb the equilibrium by increasing [Ac$^-$(aq)]. This means that the value of the expression on the right-hand side of Equation 8.13 becomes greater than the equilibrium value of 1.8 × 10^{-5} mol litre^{-1}.

To return to equilibrium, the value of this expression must be lowered. The only way that this can be achieved is for Ac$^-$(aq) to combine with H$^+$(aq) to form HAc(aq). In this way [Ac$^-$(aq)] is reduced.

⬤ How will the other concentrations, [H$^+$(aq)] and [HAc(aq)], change, and what effect will these changes have on the expression on the right-hand side of Equation 8.13?

○ A reduction in [Ac$^-$(aq)] must be accompanied by an equivalent reduction in [H$^+$(aq)]. At the same time [HAc(aq)] increases. Both of these changes lead to a reduction in the value of the expression on the right-hand side of Equation 8.13.

These changes, which involve a shift in the overall composition of the reaction mixture to the left in Equation 7.9, continue until the value of the expression on the right-hand side of Equation 8.13 once again becomes 1.8×10^{-5} mol litre^{-1}. Equilibrium is re-established. Our discussion is entirely consistent with the prediction we made earlier using Le Chatelier's principle. Focusing on the equilibrium expression, however, emphasizes that it is the *fixed value of the equilibrium constant* that determines which changes occur.

8.3.4 Changes in temperature: the equilibrium constant

A change in temperature can have a marked effect on the composition of an equilibrium mixture for a reaction in solution. The effect will depend, as in the case for gas-phase reactions (Section 8.2.2), on whether the reaction is endothermic or exothermic, and it can be predicted using Le Chatelier's principle. Indeed, the flow diagram in Figure 8.5, which summarizes the effect of temperature on an equilibrium mixture in the gas phase, is equally applicable to solution reactions.

⬤ The thermochemical equation for the dissociation of hypochlorous acid, HClO, in water is:

$$HClO(aq) \rightleftharpoons H^+(aq) + ClO^-(aq) \quad \Delta H = +13.8 \text{ kJ} \qquad (8.22)$$

How will the equilibrium yield of H$^+$(aq) change with increasing temperature?

○ The reaction is endothermic in the forward direction. The equilibrium yield of H$^+$(aq) will increase as the temperature is raised (Figure 8.5).

The change in composition of an equilibrium mixture with temperature arises because *the equilibrium constant itself depends on temperature*. This is why it is important to state the temperature when the equilibrium constant for a particular reaction is quoted.

For any chemical reaction at a given temperature the equilibrium constant has a specific *fixed* numerical value.

We shall not go into details but it is worth noting that the magnitude of the equilibrium constant for a reaction that is endothermic in the forward direction always becomes larger as the temperature is raised. A larger value of an equilibrium constant indicates that the equilibrium position for a reaction moves towards favouring the products rather than the reactants (Section 8.3.2). This is consistent with the prediction that would be arrived at using Le Chatelier's principle as illustrated, for example, by the dissociation of hypochlorous acid above.

The magnitude of the equilibrium constant for a reaction that is exothermic in the forward direction always becomes smaller as the temperature is raised.

○ Is this consistent with the prediction that would be arrived at using Le Chatelier's principle?

○ For an exothermic reaction, Le Chatelier's principle would predict a decrease in the equilibrium yield of a product with increasing temperature. This is consistent with a smaller value of the equilibrium constant, which indicates that the equilibrium position for the reaction moves towards favouring the reactants rather than the products.

Question 8.4 Iodic acid dissociates in water according to the equation:

$$HIO_3(aq) \rightleftharpoons H^+(aq) + IO_3^-(aq) \tag{8.23}$$

Table 8.2 provides information about the concentrations of $HIO_3(aq)$, $H^+(aq)$ and $IO_3^-(aq)$ for a particular equilibrium mixture as the temperature is raised from 25 °C to 45 °C.

(a) At each temperature calculate the value of the equilibrium constant K.

(b) Is the dissociation of iodic acid in water exothermic or endothermic in the forward direction? ◀

Table 8.2 Equilibrium molar concentrations in a particular equilibrium mixture of iodic acid in water at 25 °C and 45 °C.

Temperature	$\dfrac{[HIO_3(aq)]}{\text{mol litre}^{-1}}$	$\dfrac{[H^+(aq)]}{\text{mol litre}^{-1}}$	$\dfrac{[IO_3^-(aq)]}{\text{mol litre}^{-1}}$
25 °C	0.029	0.071	0.071
45 °C	0.034	0.066	0.066

8.4 Carbon dioxide gas and water

Part of the carbon cycle (Block 2) involves the transfer of carbon dioxide from the atmosphere to surface waters. The dissolved carbon dioxide gas, $CO_2(aq)$, undergoes a complex sequence of reactions that results in carbon being present in oceans and fresh waters in several different chemical forms. One of the most important is the hydrogen carbonate ion, HCO_3^-, also called the bicarbonate ion. To gain a complete picture of the chemistry of carbon in oceans and fresh waters, it would be necessary to consider all of the equilibria involving carbon in all of its chemical forms present in solution. Nonetheless, some useful insights can be obtained by looking at the first step alone, that is the dissolution of carbon dioxide. This can be represented by the chemical equation:

$$CO_2(g) \rightleftharpoons CO_2(aq) \tag{8.24}$$

The expression for the equilibrium constant for this reaction is:

$$K = \frac{[CO_2(aq)]}{[CO_2(g)]} \tag{8.25}$$

This is of the same form as the equilibrium relationships you have met previously for reactions in solution, but now the reactant CO_2 is a gas. In line with the definition of concentration in solution, we can define the concentration of a gas as the number of moles of gas molecules in a volume of one litre. So, in the case of carbon dioxide gas in the atmosphere, the concentration is the number of moles of carbon dioxide gas molecules in one litre of atmosphere. We can calculate an average value for this concentration from information given in Block 2. In Table 6.2 of that block, you were told that the number of particles of carbon dioxide in one cubic metre of atmosphere is 9.2×10^{21}. In Block 6, you learnt that these particles are in fact molecules and that one mole of carbon dioxide contains 6.02×10^{23} molecules.

How many moles of carbon dioxide molecules are there in one cubic metre of atmosphere?

There are 9.2×10^{21} molecules in one cubic metre. This is

$$\frac{9.2 \times 10^{21}}{6.02 \times 10^{23}} \text{ mol} = 1.5 \times 10^{-2} \text{ mol}$$

One litre is a thousandth of a cubic metre, so the concentration of carbon dioxide gas in the atmosphere is 1.5×10^{-5} mol litre^{-1}.

In Block 2 it was stated that the amount of carbon dioxide gas that can dissolve in surface waters is limited. You can now see that one factor that contributes to this limit is the equilibrium relationship in Equation 8.25.

If the concentration of carbon dioxide in the atmosphere is increased, for example by burning fossil fuels and clearing forests, this will affect the equilibrium in Equation 8.24. According to Le Chatelier's principle such an increase will tend to move the equilibrium position over to the right in order to minimize this change. This means that more carbon dioxide gas will dissolve. We can reach the same conclusion by considering the equilibrium relationship. The immediate effect of an increase of $[CO_2(g)]$ will be to *reduce* the value of the expression on the right-hand side of Equation 8.25, making it *smaller* than the value of the equilibrium constant. A re-adjustment therefore occurs; $[CO_2(aq)]$ increases and $[CO_2(g)]$ decreases, and this continues until the expression on the right-hand side of Equation 8.25 once again has the same magnitude as the equilibrium constant.

Any increase in the amount of carbon dioxide gas in the atmosphere will not all be taken up by the oceans and fresh waters. The increase will be shared, in a manner dictated by the magnitude of the equilibrium constant, between the gas and the solution phase. However, remember that this conclusion is arrived at by considering the equilibrium in Equation 8.24 in isolation. As already indicated, this is actually just one part of a complex sequence of reactions. Predicting the exact capacity of oceans and fresh waters to dissolve carbon dioxide gas is an important, but very difficult, problem.

A more familiar example, perhaps, of the dissolution of carbon dioxide in water is fizzy drinks and sparkling mineral waters. Fizzy (or carbonated) drinks contain a greater concentration of dissolved carbon dioxide than water in equilibrium with the atmosphere. In the unopened bottle or can, the drink and the gas above it are at high pressure.

○ How does increasing the pressure of carbon dioxide gas above the drink maintain the increased concentration of dissolved carbon dioxide gas?

○ The *equilibrium* concentration of carbon dioxide gas will be higher the greater the pressure of carbon dioxide. In turn, this will mean that the equilibrium concentration of *dissolved* carbon dioxide gas will be higher, so the equilibrium constant in Equation 8.25 maintains a *fixed* value.

Fizzy drinks were introduced in Europe in the late 1700s. These early drinks were made by bubbling carbon dioxide through water. The carbon dioxide was produced in the way that you met in Section 2.4.2 of Block 6, the action of acid on calcium carbonate. Later drinks had sugar, flavouring and colouring added to the water. In 1772, Joseph Priestley published a paper entitled 'Directions for impregnating water with fixed air' (fixed air was the term then used for carbon dioxide) in which he gave a detailed procedure for making fizzy drinks and recognized that the amount of carbon dioxide dissolved in the drink was increased by increasing the pressure of carbon dioxide above the water. In modern fizzy drink plants, carbon dioxide gas under pressure is dissolved in chilled water (containing sweetener, flavouring and colouring if required).

● For the equilibrium

$$CO_2(g) \rightleftharpoons CO_2(aq) \tag{8.24}$$

the reaction in the forward direction is exothermic. Why do fizzy drink manufacturers use chilled water?

○ Since the reaction is exothermic in the forward direction, the equilibrium concentration of $CO_2(aq)$ will increase with decreasing temperature. Hence, there will be more fizz in the drink.

Question 8.5   The sparkling mineral waters found on the supermarket shelf are generally still mineral waters that have been treated like fizzy drinks to make them carbonated. There are however some mineral waters that are naturally slightly fizzy. These are formed underground in places where it is cooler than at the surface and where decaying organic matter produces a higher pressure of carbon dioxide locally. How do these conditions result in the water being carbonated? ◄

8.5   Summary of Section 8

1   Chemical equilibrium represents a state of dynamic balance.

2   The response of an equilibrium mixture to a change in conditions can be predicted using Le Chatelier's principle. This states that when a system in equilibrium is subject to an external constraint, the system responds in a way that tends to oppose the effect of the constraint.

3   The proportion of a product in an equilibrium mixture can be referred to as the equilibrium yield of that substance.

4   The effect of pressure changes on an equilibrium mixture involving gases only is summarized in Figure 8.4.

5   The nature of the response of an equilibrium mixture to a change in temperature depends on whether the reaction is exothermic or endothermic. Figure 8.5 summarizes the behaviour.

6   For a solution reaction at constant temperature, changing the concentration of a particular substance in the equilibrium mixture results in the concentrations of other substances in the mixture also changing. Le Chatelier's principle can be used to determine whether the change in the composition of the equilibrium mixture corresponds to moving the reaction to the left or to the right.

7   The equilibrium relationship for a reaction involves the equilibrium constant K and the *equilibrium* molar concentrations of the reactants and products. For the dissociation of an acid HX,

$$HX(aq) \rightleftharpoons H^+(aq) + X^-(aq)$$

the equilibrium constant is

$$K = \frac{\left[H^+(aq)\right]\left[X^-(aq)\right]}{\left[HX(aq)\right]}$$

8   The magnitude of the equilibrium constant for a given reaction is related to how far the reaction will proceed before equilibrium is reached. If the magnitude is large the equilibrium position will strongly favour the formation of products; if it is small then reactants will be favoured.

9   The form of the equilibrium expression for a given solution reaction can be used to predict what will happen when the concentration of a particular substance in the equilibrium mixture is changed at constant temperature. This approach emphasizes that it is the fixed value of the equilibrium constant that determines the changes that occur in the overall composition of the equilibrium mixture.

10 For any chemical reaction at a given temperature, the equilibrium constant has a specific fixed numerical value. For an increase in temperature, the magnitude of the equilibrium constant decreases for a reaction that is exothermic in the forward direction and increases for a reaction that is endothermic in the forward direction.

Acids and bases: a quantitative view

In Section 7 we set out to take a more detailed look at the role that water plays in chemistry. There is no doubt that water is of central importance as a solvent. A particular aspect of this role is that when certain substances dissolve in water they dissociate to give hydrogen ions, and so reveal their acidic properties. In this context we discussed the equilibrium properties of strong and weak acids in water in Section 8. However, in all of our account so far, we have implicitly assumed that water simply acts as a background medium. For the examples that we have selected this assumption is acceptable, but to develop a broader view a very significant modification is required. It is that water itself can break down to a small extent to produce ions. The amounts involved are tiny; roughly for every 550 million water molecules in water at room temperature just one will have dissociated into ions. Nonetheless as we shall see, there are important implications for the properties of acidic and basic solutions.

⬤ If you were to test the electrical conductivity of pure water using the apparatus described in Block 6, Section 13.2 and Figure 4.1 of this block, do you think that it would conduct electricity sufficiently well to ring the bell or light the bulb?

◯ No; as you saw in Section 4, water does not conduct electricity sufficiently well to cause either of these events.

As in the case of acetic acid dissolved in water (Section 7.3.1), this does not mean that there are no ions in solution but simply that, if present, their concentrations are relatively small. We know that water and electricity can make a lethal combination. Water in contact with mains wiring is dangerous because it can result in an electric shock; this indicates that water conducts electricity, and supports the idea that water contains *some* ions.

The ions that are present in pure water are the hydrogen ion, $H^+(aq)$, and the hydroxide ion, $OH^-(aq)$. They are involved in the following equilibrium reaction:

$$H_2O(l) \rightleftharpoons H^+(aq) + OH^-(aq) \tag{9.1}$$

Thus pure water is a medium that is mainly water molecules, $H_2O(l)$, with tiny amounts of $H^+(aq)$ and $OH^-(aq)$ ions also present. The equilibrium position lies well over to the left in Equation 9.1.

⬤ In Block 6 you met the idea of neutralization. What are the key features of this process?

◯ Neutralization reactions take the form 'acid + base → salt + water'. Underlying all such reactions is the combination of hydrogen ions, provided by the acid, and hydroxide ions, provided by the base, to form water. In Block 6, this was called the fundamental neutralization reaction and it was represented as:

$$H^+(aq) + OH^-(aq) \longrightarrow H_2O(l)$$

This reaction was assumed to go to completion.

You can see now that the fundamental neutralization reaction corresponds to the *reverse* direction (right to left) of the reaction in Equation 9.1. The fact that the equilibrium position in Equation 9.1 lies well over to the left is consistent with our earlier view that neutralization effectively involves hydrogen and hydroxide ions combining completely to give water.

9.1 The ion product of water

The form of the equilibrium expressed by Equation 9.1 bears a close resemblance to that for the dissociation of a weak acid as described in Section 8. In fact an equilibrium relationship, involving an equilibrium constant, can be written in the same way. It is:

$$K = \frac{[H^+(aq)][OH^-(aq)]}{[H_2O(l)]} \tag{9.2}$$

Would you expect the magnitude of the equilibrium constant for pure water at room temperature to be large or small?

Since the equilibrium position lies well over to the left in Equation 9.1, the magnitude of K will be very small.

In Equation 9.2, the terms $[H^+(aq)]$ and $[OH^-(aq)]$ represent equilibrium molar ion concentrations. The term $[H_2O(l)]$ is also an equilibrium concentration, but of water itself! Literally it is the number of moles of water molecules in one litre of pure water. If we ignore the minute amount of water that breaks down into ions, then at a given temperature $[H_2O(l)]$ must represent a fixed concentration: you cannot increase or decrease the amount of pure water in a fixed volume.

By convention it is usual to rearrange the equilibrium relationship in Equation 9.2 by taking the fixed term $[H_2O(l)]$ over to the left-hand side, that is:

$$K[H_2O(l)] = [H^+(aq)][OH^-(aq)]$$

The combination $K[H_2O(l)]$ is then itself a constant at a fixed temperature. It is given both a special name, the **ion product** of water, and a special symbol, K_w. So, finally, we have:

$$K_w = [H^+(aq)][OH^-(aq)] \tag{9.3}$$

The experimental value of the ion product of water at 25 °C is 1.0×10^{-14} mol^2 litre^{-2}. It is useful to consider the implications of this value, both for pure water and for solutions of acids and bases.

Pure water

What is the equilibrium concentration of hydrogen ions, $[H^+(aq)]$, in water at 25 °C?

Each water molecule that dissociates gives one hydrogen ion and one hydroxide ion. Thus the numbers, and hence the concentrations, of these ions at equilibrium will be the same, that is $[H^+(aq)] = [OH^-(aq)]$. To find the equilibrium concentration of hydrogen ions, the term $[OH^-(aq)]$ in Equation 9.3 is replaced by $[H^+(aq)]$, so that

$$K_w = [H^+(aq)] \times [H^+(aq)]$$

or

$$1.0 \times 10^{-14}\, \text{mol}^2\, \text{litre}^{-2} = [H^+(aq)] \times [H^+(aq)]$$

The equilibrium hydrogen ion concentration is found by taking the square root of both sides of this equation:

$$[H^+(aq)] = \sqrt{1.0 \times 10^{-14}\, \text{mol}^2\, \text{litre}^{-2}}$$

$$= 1.0 \times 10^{-7}\, \text{mol litre}^{-1}$$

The value you measured for the concentration of hydrogen ions in tap water in Activity 7.1 should have been not too far from this value.

The hydrogen and hydroxide ion concentrations in pure water at 25 °C are equal: $[H^+(aq)] = [OH^-(aq)] = 1.0 \times 10^{-7}$ mol litre^{-1}. These concentrations are very small, but they cannot be dismissed lightly, as we shall see.

Water can be viewed as possessing both acidic and basic hydroxide properties because, when it dissociates, both hydrogen ions and hydroxide ions are produced. However, these two types of ion are always produced in equal numbers. Thus the acidic nature of water is always balanced by its basic nature. We say that it is *neutral*.

In a wider context, the idea of neutrality can be applied to any aqueous solution in which the hydrogen and hydroxide ion concentrations are equal. To be more specific, at 25 °C a **neutral solution** is defined as one in which the hydrogen ion concentration is 1.0×10^{-7} mol litre^{-1}.

Solutions of acids and bases

It is worth re-emphasizing that the ion product of water at 25 °C has a *fixed* magnitude. In practice, this means that there is a limitation on the concentrations of hydrogen and hydroxide ions that can co-exist in *any* solution for which water is the solvent at 25 °C. Whatever the individual concentrations of hydrogen ions and hydroxide ions, they must satisfy the relationship in Equation 9.3; that is, when multiplied together they must give a result equal to K_w.

Suppose we prepare a solution of hydrochloric acid at 25 °C by dissolving 0.10 mol of hydrogen chloride in sufficient water to make one litre of solution. Since hydrochloric acid is a strong acid, it will effectively dissociate completely into ions. The concentration of hydrogen ions that has been 'added' to the water is equivalent therefore to 0.10 mol litre^{-1}. This concentration far outweighs the concentration of hydrogen ions already present due to the dissociation of water itself. It is therefore perfectly valid to ignore any contribution of the latter and to take the hydrogen ion concentration in the solution to be 0.10 mol litre^{-1}. It is only ever necessary to consider a contribution from the dissociation of water itself when an 'added' hydrogen ion concentration is close to or less than the neutral value of 1.0×10^{-7} mol litre^{-1}. This is of more theoretical than practical interest and will not be considered further.

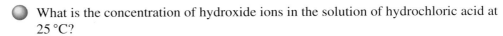 What is the concentration of hydroxide ions in the solution of hydrochloric acid at 25 °C?

We know that at 25 °C

$$1.0 \times 10^{-14} \text{ mol}^2 \text{ litre}^{-2} = [H^+(aq)][OH^-(aq)]$$

so we can rearrange this equation to find $[OH^-(aq)]$,

$$[OH^-(aq)] = \frac{1.0 \times 10^{-14} \text{ mol}^2 \text{ litre}^{-2}}{[H^+(aq)]}$$

Since the solution in question has $[H^+(aq)] = 0.10$ mol litre^{-1}, then

$$[OH^-(aq)] = \frac{1.0 \times 10^{-14} \text{ mol}^2 \text{ litre}^{-2}}{0.10 \text{ mol litre}^{-1}}$$

$$= 1.0 \times 10^{-13} \text{ mol litre}^{-1}$$

Thus, in an acidic solution of 0.10 mol litre^{-1} there is a very small, but nonetheless finite, concentration of hydroxide ions.

○ What is the concentration of hydrogen ions in a solution of the base sodium hydroxide in water in which the hydroxide ion concentration, [OH$^-$(aq)], is 0.10 mol litre^{-1} at 25 °C?

○ There are direct parallels here with the calculation we have carried out above for hydrochloric acid. In this case we have:

$$[H^+(aq)] = \frac{1.0 \times 10^{-14} \, mol^2 \, litre^{-2}}{[OH^-(aq)]}$$

Since [OH$^-$(aq)] = 0.10 mol litre^{-1}, it follows that [H$^+$(aq)] = 1.0×10^{-13} mol litre^{-1}.

So, in a basic solution of 0.10 mol litre^{-1} there is a very small, but nonetheless finite, concentration of hydrogen ions.

Overall, a picture of solutions of acids and bases begins to emerge in which there is a type of 'see-saw effect'. If the hydrogen ion concentration is high then the hydroxide ion concentration will be correspondingly low, and vice versa. At heart, this behaviour is due to the form of the relationship in Equation 9.3.

○ If a solution has a hydrogen ion concentration greater than 1.0×10^{-7} mol litre^{-1}, will the hydroxide ion concentration be greater or less than 1.0×10^{-7} mol litre^{-1}?

○ It will be less than 1.0×10^{-7} mol litre^{-1}, as predicted by the relationship in Equation 9.3.

Thus the concentration of hydrogen ions exceeds the concentration of hydroxide ions, and the solution can be justifiably called acidic. The more the hydrogen ion concentration exceeds the neutral value of 1.0×10^{-7} mol litre^{-1}, then the more acidic is the solution.

An acidic solution can be defined as one in which the hydrogen ion concentration is *greater* than 1.0×10^{-7} mol litre^{-1}.

Strictly, this definition applies only at 25 °C because the value of the ion product for water, K_w, varies with temperature. For instance at 37 °C (human body temperature) $K_w = 2.5 \times 10^{-14}$ mol^2 litre^{-2}, so that in a neutral solution [H$^+$(aq)] = 1.6×10^{-7} mol litre^{-1}.

In a solution at 25 °C in which the hydroxide ion concentration is greater than 1.0×10^{-7} mol litre^{-1}, then the hydrogen ion concentration will be correspondingly less than this value. In this case we can justifiably call the solution basic. A basic solution could thus be defined as one in which the hydroxide ion concentration is greater than 1.0×10^{-7} mol litre^{-1} at 25 °C. However, it is more useful to phrase the definition in terms of the hydrogen ion concentration.

A basic solution can be defined as one in which the hydrogen ion concentration is *less* than 1.0×10^{-7} mol litre^{-1}.

Again, strictly, this definition applies only at 25 °C.

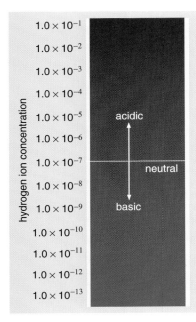

1.0×10^{-1}
1.0×10^{-2}
1.0×10^{-3}
1.0×10^{-4}
1.0×10^{-5} acidic
1.0×10^{-6}
1.0×10^{-7} neutral
1.0×10^{-8}
1.0×10^{-9} basic
1.0×10^{-10}
1.0×10^{-11}
1.0×10^{-12}
1.0×10^{-13}

hydrogen ion concentration

Figure 9.1 The hydrogen ion concentration defines whether a solution is acidic, neutral or basic.

Given a hydrogen ion concentration for a solution at 25 °C we are now in a position to state whether the solution is acidic, neutral or basic. The basis for such a decision is summarized in Figure 9.1.

Question 9.1   State, giving your reasons, whether the following aqueous solutions are acidic, neutral or basic at 25 °C. (a) NaOH of concentration 1.0×10^{-2} mol litre^{-1}; (b) HCl of concentration 1.0×10^{-5} mol litre^{-1}; (c) NaCl of concentration 1.0×10^{3} mol litre^{-1}; (d) HAc (acetic acid) of concentration 1.0 mol litre^{-1}. ◀

Question 9.2   (a) What happens to the hydrogen ion concentration when one litre of a 1.0 mol litre^{-1} solution of hydrochloric acid is fully mixed with one litre of a 1.0 mol litre^{-1} solution of sodium hydroxide?

(b) What happens to the hydrogen ion concentration when two litres of a 1.0 mol litre^{-1} solution of hydrochloric acid are fully mixed with one litre of a 1.0 mol litre^{-1} solution of sodium hydroxide. ◀

9.2   A universal scale for acidity and basicity

Most solutions encountered in the laboratory or in everyday life have hydrogen or hydroxide ion concentrations that are no greater than 1.0 mol litre^{-1}, but the concentrations can vary enormously.

○ Calculate the hydrogen ion concentration at 25 °C of typical solutions, such as 1.0 mol litre^{-1} HCl and 1.0 mol litre^{-1} NaOH. By what factor does the hydrogen ion concentration vary between the typical solutions?

○ For a 1.0 mol litre^{-1} HCl solution, [H^{+}(aq)] = 1.0 mol litre^{-1}. For a 1.0 mol litre^{-1} NaOH solution, [OH^{-}(aq)] = 1.0 mol litre^{-1} and so [H^{+}(aq)] = 1.0×10^{-14} mol litre^{-1}. The hydrogen ion concentration of these typical solutions thus varies by a factor of 10^{14}.

To handle this huge range of hydrogen ion concentrations it is convenient to introduce a simple number scale. This is the **pH scale**. It was introduced in 1909 by the Danish biochemist Soren Sorensen, who at the time was director of chemistry at the Carlsberg Laboratory.

One way of viewing the pH scale is that it is based on the power of ten of the hydrogen ion concentration in a given solution. Thus, if the hydrogen ion concentration is written as 1×10^{-n} mol litre^{-1}, then the pH is simply equal to n. For example, if a hydrogen ion concentration is 1.0×10^{-2} mol litre^{-1} then the value of n is 2 and the corresponding pH is also 2. A pH scale derived on this basis is shown in Figure 9.2: for completeness, both the hydrogen ion *and* the hydroxide ion concentrations in a given solution are shown. For example, a pH of 4 corresponds to a hydrogen ion concentration of 1.0×10^{-4} mol litre^{-1} and a hydroxide ion concentration of 1.0×10^{-10} mol litre^{-1}. As you would expect, multiplying these two concentrations together gives 1.0×10^{-14} mol^2 litre^{-2}, the ion product of water.

● From the definitions given earlier, what values will the pH take in (a) a neutral solution, (b) an acidic solution and (c) a basic solution?

○ At 25 °C a neutral solution is defined as one in which the hydrogen ion concentration is 1.0×10^{-7} mol litre^{-1}. The value of n is 7 and so a neutral solution has pH of 7. At 25 °C an acidic solution has a hydrogen ion concentration greater than 1.0×10^{-7} mol litre^{-1}. The value of n will decrease

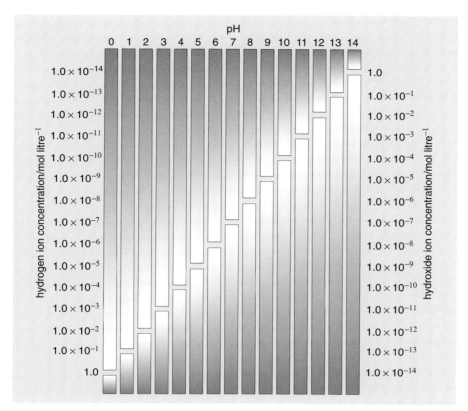

Figure 9.2 The pH scale. The lengths of the bars at the top represent the hydrogen ion concentration, read from the scale on the left. The lengths of the bars at the bottom represent the hydroxide ion concentration, read from the scale on the right.

with increasing hydrogen ion concentration. (If you are uncertain about this see Figure 9.2.) Thus the pH of an acidic solution will be *less* than 7. At 25 °C a basic solution has a hydrogen ion concentration that is less than 1.0×10^{-7} mol litre^{-1}. This means the pH will be *greater* than 7.

Increasingly, the term pH is creeping into everyday language (Figure 9.3). For instance, it is used in connection with commercial products such as bath foam or face wash that claim to have a pH the same as your skin (the value given is about the same as the pH of rain water). Other similar products claim that they are mild or pure because they have neutral pH, that is 7. The pH scale was also given inside the book of indicator papers that was used for the determination of hydrogen ion concentration via colour change in Activity 7.1.

Given the pH of a solution it is possible to work backwards and determine the hydrogen ion concentration. If the pH is equal to n, then the hydrogen ion concentration will be 1.0×10^{-n} mol litre^{-1}, that is ten to the power of minus the pH.

○ Without referring to Figure 9.2, state the hydrogen ion concentration of a solution with a pH of (a) 3 and (b) 11.

○ (a) If the pH is 3 then the hydrogen ion concentration is 1.0×10^{-3} mol litre^{-1}.
   (b) If the pH is 11 then the hydrogen ion concentration is 1.0×10^{-11} mol litre^{-1}.

Figure 9.3 A bottle of bath foam; note the pH value of 5.5.

79

Question 9.3   Without referring to Figure 9.2 determine the pH of each of the solutions (a) to (c) in Question 9.1. Do these agree with the pHs expected for basic, acidic and neutral solutions? ◀

9.3   Summary of Section 9

1   Pure water dissociates to give very small concentrations of hydrogen ions, $H^+(aq)$, and hydroxide ions, $OH^-(aq)$. The equilibrium position for the dissociation reaction

$$H_2O(l) \rightleftharpoons H^+(aq) + OH^-(aq)$$

lies well over to the left.

2   The ion product of water is defined by the relationship

$$K_w = [H^+(aq)][OH^-(aq)]$$

At 25 °C the experimental value of K_w is 1.0×10^{-14} $mol^2\,litre^{-2}$.

3   The ion product of water controls the concentrations of hydrogen and hydroxide ions that can co-exist in any solution at a given temperature.

4   In pure water, or any neutral solution, at 25 °C

$$[H^+(aq)] = [OH^-(aq)] = 1.0 \times 10^{-7}\,mol\,litre^{-1}$$

5   An acidic solution is one in which the hydrogen ion concentration is greater than 1.0×10^{-7} $mol\,litre^{-1}$ at 25 °C. A basic solution is one in which the hydrogen ion concentration is less than 1.0×10^{-7} $mol\,litre^{-1}$ at 25 °C.

6   One way of expressing the pH scale is to write a hydrogen ion concentration as 1.0×10^{-n} $mol\,litre^{-1}$. The pH is then equal to n. Conversely, if the pH of a solution is equal to n then the corresponding hydrogen ion concentration is 1.0×10^{-n} $mol\,litre^{-1}$.

7   At 25 °C a neutral solution has pH of 7, an acidic solution has pH less than 7 and a basic solution has pH greater than 7.

Rates of chemical reactions

10

Our discussions of chemical equilibrium have focused on the end-point of chemical reactions and on the composition of the reaction mixture when the reaction has reached equilibrium, but the speed with which the equilibrium mixture is formed can also be important. In an explosion, equilibrium is reached almost instantaneously, the reaction is over in less than a millionth of a second. At the other extreme, igneous rocks can take many thousands of years to reach their equilibrium structure and composition.

The progress of a more typical reaction is shown in Figure 10.1. This is the 'clock' reaction, which you saw demonstrated on the video 'Features of reactions' (Activity 6.1), in which peroxodisulfate ions, $S_2O_8^{2-}$, react with iodide ions to produce sulfate ions and iodine:

$$S_2O_8^{2-}(aq) + 2I^-(aq) \rightleftharpoons 2SO_4^{2-}(aq) + I_2(aq) \tag{10.1}$$

The concentration of iodine is zero at the start of the reaction when solutions containing iodide ions and peroxodisulfate ions are mixed together. As the reaction proceeds, the concentration of iodine in the solution gradually builds up until its equilibrium concentration is reached. Once this value is reached, no further change in the concentration is observed.

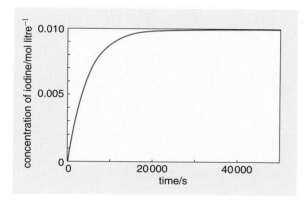

Figure 10.1   The increase in the concentration of iodine, I_2(aq), as a function of time as the reaction in Equation 10.1 progresses to equilibrium, at 25 °C.

A curve such as that in Figure 10.1 represents the progress of a reaction under a given set of reaction conditions. The slope of the first part of the curve tells us how fast the reaction is going at that time. For a faster reaction, the curve will rise more steeply and then flatten out, as equilbrium is reached, in a shorter time; for slower reactions the initial rise will be more gradual and the time before the curve flattens out will be longer. (In Figure 10.1 equilibrium is achieved in about 20 000 seconds, or 5.5 hours.) Not only do different reactions have different rates, but we can also vary the rate of a particular reaction by varying the reaction conditions.

10.1 Varying the rate of reaction

The graphs in Figure 10.2 illustrate the progress of the reaction in Equation 10.1 for a *fixed* initial concentration of iodide ions and various initial concentrations of peroxodisulfate ions.

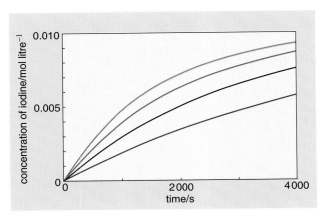

Figure 10.2   The progress of the reaction in Equation 10.1 as measured by the increase in iodine concentration at 25 °C for four initial concentrations of peroxodisulfate ions. The initial concentration increases in the order red, black, blue, green.

Does the speed of the reaction increase or decrease as the concentration of peroxodisulfate ions increases?

As the initial concentration of peroxodisulfate ions increases, the curves are steeper at short times; this means that the speed of the reaction increases.

The **rate of reaction** can be defined as the rate at which the concentration of a product increases, or the concentration of a reactant decreases. In Figure 10.2 we can measure the rate of reaction by measuring the rate at which the concentration of one of the products, iodine, increases. You can see that each curve is nearly a straight line in the early stages of the reaction. For these parts of the curves, then, the rate is given by:

$$\text{rate of reaction} = \frac{\text{increase in iodine concentration}}{\text{time elapsed}}$$

Look at the time taken for each of the reactions represented by the curves in Figure 10.2 to reach a particular concentration of iodine, say $0.002\,\text{mol litre}^{-1}$. Does the rate of reaction increase or decrease as the initial concentration of peroxodisulfate increases?

The curves in Figure 10.2 show that, as the initial concentration of peroxodisulfate increases, the time taken for the reaction to reach a particular concentration of iodine decreases, which means that the rate of reaction has increased.

This reaction, like many others, can be made to go faster by increasing the initial concentration of one of the reactants. Varying the concentration is thus one way in which we can alter the rate of reaction.

Another way to change the rate of a reaction is to vary the temperature. This is an effect you have probably come across in everyday life. A good example is the cooking of vegetables. The boiling temperature of water depends on the pressure of the atmosphere above the water. If you cook your vegetables in an ordinary saucepan, then the reaction (cooking) takes place at 100 °C. In a pressure cooker, the boiling temperature rises to 112 °C and your vegetables will cook in a third of the time. Should you be cooking your vegetables near the top of a mountain, where atmospheric pressure is reduced, the temperature of the boiling water will be lower and you will have a long wait for your dinner.

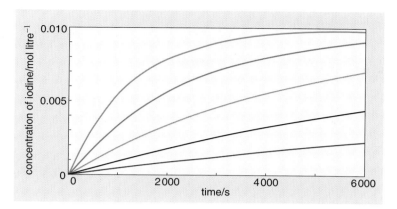

Figure 10.3 How the rate of the reaction in Equation 10.1 varies with temperature. The progress of the reaction is plotted as in Figure 10.2 but this time the initial concentrations of both of the reactants are fixed, and the different curves correspond to different temperatures; the temperature increases in the order red, black, brown, blue, green.

○ Look at the time taken for each of the reactions represented by the curves in Figure 10.3 to reach a particular concentration of iodine. Does the rate of reaction increase or decrease as the temperature increases?

○ The time taken for any chosen concentration of iodine to be produced decreases as the temperature increases; this means that the rate of reaction increases with increasing temperature.

This reaction, like our cooking example, can thus be made to go faster by raising the temperature. You have now met two ways in which the rate of a given reaction can be altered. In the next sections we shall consider *why* reaction rates depend on concentration and temperature.

10.2 Getting together: the effect of concentration

A fundamental requirement for molecules to react is that they come into contact with each other. In Activity 8.1, you saw that reactant molecules could form product molecules only if they collided with each other, and this is true for all molecules reacting in the gaseous state. Reactions of solids can be slow because of the difficulty that reactant molecules in the centre of a solid have in reaching other reactant molecules. Reaction can be speeded up by dissolving the reactants, because the molecules can then encounter each other more easily. The more concentrated the solution, the greater the probability of reactant molecules encountering each other; consequently, reactions in solution often go faster as the initial concentrations of reactants increase. Similarly, reactions in the gaseous state usually go faster if the pressure of the reactant gases is increased, because the molecules will collide more often.

Question 10.1 The reaction of ammonia with oxygen (from the air) to form nitrogen monoxide (NO) is the first stage in the industrial conversion of ammonia into nitric acid. The chemical equation for this is:

$$4NH_3(g) + 5O_2(g) \rightleftharpoons 4NO(g) + 6H_2O(g)$$

This reaction is operated at a pressure of five times atmospheric pressure (5 atmospheres). What does this suggest about the effect of pressure on the rate of this reaction? ◀

One reason why the rate of a reaction might be slow is that the reactant molecules do not encounter each other very often. However, simply ensuring that the reactant molecules come together is not sufficient to ensure reaction. Usually only a fraction of encounters result in product formation.

10.3 Energy and reaction

It's easier to understand why not all encounters lead to reaction if we consider *how* reactant molecules are transformed into product molecules. This is best achieved by considering a simple reaction. In the atmosphere, ultraviolet radiation from the Sun can break one of the O—H bonds in the water molecule to form a hydrogen atom, H, and a hydroxyl molecule, OH. The latter can react with an oxygen atom (formed by breaking bonds in other oxygen-containing molecules) to form an oxygen molecule and a hydrogen atom:

$$O(g) + OH(g) \rightleftharpoons O_2(g) + H(g) \tag{10.2}$$

This reaction passes through an intervening stage, at the instant of encounter, in which the O—H bond in the hydroxyl molecule is partially broken and an O—O bond in the oxygen molecule is partially formed. This intervening stage is *not* a stable molecule: its internal energy is *higher* than that of either the products or the reactants. Figure 10.4 shows how the internal energy changes as the oxygen atom and hydroxyl molecule react.

Figure 10.4 A schematic representation of how the internal energy changes during the process in Equation 10.2.

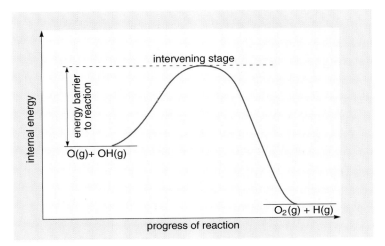

As can be seen from this diagram, before the products can form, the reactant molecules must gain enough energy to reach the intervening stage. In this case the energy is supplied by the kinetic energy when the oxygen atom and hydroxyl molecule collide. If, when they collide, the kinetic energy available is insufficient to enable the intervening stage to form, then reaction does not occur. The oxygen atom and hydroxyl molecule simply bounce off each other. Thus only encounters involving sufficient energy lead to reaction. Another way of describing this is to say that there is an **energy barrier** to reaction such that products can form only if reactant molecules gain enough energy to surmount the barrier.

Energy barriers exist for *every* chemical reaction, not just for simple reactions like the one in Equation 10.2. Figure 10.5 shows schematic representations for a general exothermic reaction and a general endothermic reaction. Irrespective of whether energy is released or gained overall, there is always an energy barrier that reactant molecules must overcome.

> Every chemical reaction has an energy barrier that must be overcome before the reactant molecules can form products.

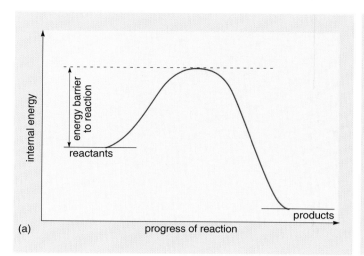
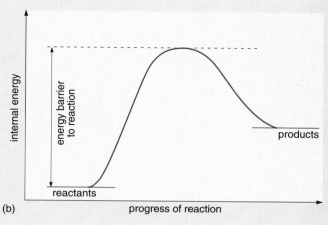

Figure 10.5   Schematic representations of the energy barriers that must be overcome for (a) a general exothermic reaction and (b) a general endothermic reaction.

Question 10.2   The thermochemical equation for the reaction in Equation 10.1 is:

$$S_2O_8^{2-}(aq) + 2I^-(aq) \rightleftharpoons 2SO_4^{2-}(aq) + I_2(aq) \quad \Delta H = -341\,kJ$$

Sketch and label a schematic representation of the internal energy changes that occur in this reaction, similar to that in Figure 10.4. ◀

10.4 The effect of temperature on the rate of reaction

The energy needed to surmount the energy barrier generally comes from the kinetic energy of the reactant molecules. However, only a fraction of encounters involve sufficient kinetic energy to overcome the energy barrier and lead to reaction. In Block 5, you saw that the molecules in a gas have a range of speeds, and their mean speed increases as the temperature increases.

⬤   How will the proportion of molecules with large amounts of kinetic energy vary with temperature?

◯   Molecules with high speeds will have high kinetic energies (Block 5) and so the fraction of molecules with high kinetic energy increases with increasing temperature.

If more molecules have high kinetic energy, then the probability that an encounter involves sufficient energy to overcome the energy barrier will be higher and so reaction will be faster. Molecules in solution also have a distribution of speeds and so similar arguments apply to reactions in solution. Thus, as the temperature is raised, the rate of reaction increases because more encounters have sufficient energy to overcome the energy barrier. We can draw a general conclusion about the effect of temperature on reaction rate:

The rate of any chemical reaction can be increased by raising the temperature at which the reaction takes place.

Question 10.3   The thermochemical equation for the reaction of sulfur dioxide with oxygen to form sulfur trioxide is:

$$2SO_2(g) + O_2(g) \rightleftharpoons 2SO_3(g) \quad \Delta H = -198\,kJ$$

This process is operated at 500 °C. Does operating at this temperature increase the equilibrium yield above that which would be obtained at room temperature? If not, why is a high operating temperature used? ◄

Question 10.3 illustrates an important point: the conditions that maximize the proportion of product at equilibrium may not be those that allow the reaction to proceed at a convenient rate.

Like the example in Question 10.3, many industrially important reactions are exothermic but are run at high temperatures to increase the rate. A way of increasing the rate without raising the temperature would therefore be very useful, and this is the subject of the next section.

10.5 Help from outside: catalysts

On the video 'Features of reactions' (Activity 6.1), it was shown that the rate of decomposition of hydrogen peroxide at room temperature could be increased by the addition of small amounts of several substances, such as iron oxide, manganese oxide, and liver. In this demonstration the hydrogen peroxide completely decomposed in each case, but the rate at which this happened varied considerably. However, at the end of the reactions, the added substances were still present in the same amount. The sole effect of these substances was to speed up the reaction; they did not alter the equilibrium position nor were they used up in the reaction. Such substances are called **catalysts**.

> A catalyst is a substance that increases the rate of reaction but is not itself used up during the reaction.

Although the internal energy of the reactants and products of a reaction is fixed, the path by which the two are interconnected is not. There are often several possible routes by which a reaction may take place. The way a catalyst works is by providing an alternative lower energy pathway, as shown in Figure 10.6 for the decomposition of hydrogen peroxide, H_2O_2:

$$2H_2O_2(aq) \rightleftharpoons 2H_2O(l) + O_2(g) \tag{10.3}$$

In the presence of a catalyst (curve b) the intervening stage is of lower energy and thus the energy barrier is lower. Curve b shows what happens with one catalyst: in the video, you saw that different catalysts speeded up the reaction by different amounts.

Figure 10.7 shows the energy barriers for the reaction of nitrogen and hydrogen to form ammonia, using three different catalysts:

$$N_2(g) + 3H_2(g) \rightleftharpoons 2NH_3(g) \tag{10.4}$$

An important point to note is that the internal energies of the reactants and products are the same whichever catalyst is used.

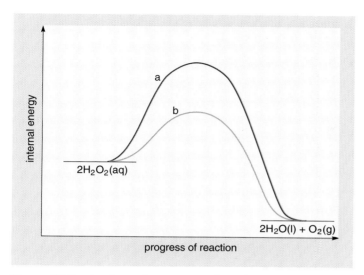

Figure 10.6 A schematic representation of the decomposition of hydrogen peroxide shown in Equation 10.3 (a) in the absence and (b) in the presence of a catalyst.

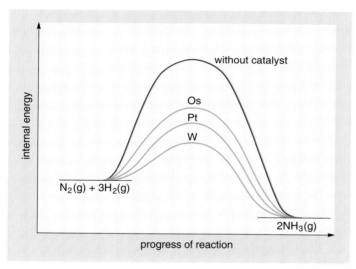

Figure 10.7 A schematic representation of the formation of ammonia (Equation 10.4) with different catalysts osmium (Os), platinum (Pt) and tungsten (W), and without a catalyst.

This reaction is of great practical importance and you will study it further in Section 11. Finding a suitable catalyst was a determining factor in developing a viable commercial process for the production of ammonia, and catalysts are crucial ingredients in many other processes in the chemical industry.

To consolidate all that you have learned about equilibrium and rates of reaction, you should now attempt Activity 10.1.

Activity 10.1 *Maximizing the yield of a product: a compromise between rate and equilibrium*

This activity examines how you choose the right conditions for a reaction to maximize the product yield whilst ensuring a reasonable rate of reaction. ◀

Question 10.4   The production of hydrogen cyanide from methane and ammonia is represented by the following thermochemical equation:

$$CH_4(g) + NH_3(g) \rightleftharpoons HCN(g) + 3H_2(g) \quad \Delta H = +256 \text{ kJ}$$

(a) Sketch a diagram showing how the internal energy changes as the reaction progresses.

(b) At normal temperatures and pressures, the equilibrium yield of hydrogen cyanide is too low for the reaction to be useful. Would any of the following improve the equilibrium yield: (i) raising the temperature; (ii) increasing the pressure in the reaction vessel; (iii) using a catalyst? ◀

Question 10.5   In the catalytic converters in modern car exhaust systems, carbon monoxide and nitrogen monoxide react to produce nitrogen and carbon dioxide. The thermochemical equation for this reaction is:

$$2CO(g) + 2NO(g) \rightleftharpoons N_2(g) + 2CO_2(g) \quad \Delta H = -747 \text{ kJ} \tag{10.5}$$

If the exhaust gases are simply released without passing over the catalytic converter, they react with oxygen in the atmosphere to form carbon dioxide and nitrogen dioxide. The thermochemical equations for these reactions are:

$$2CO(g) + O_2(g) \rightleftharpoons 2CO_2(g) \quad \Delta H = -566 \text{ kJ} \tag{10.6}$$

$$2NO(g) + O_2(g) \rightleftharpoons 2NO_2(g) \quad \Delta H = -114 \text{ kJ} \tag{10.7}$$

(a) How will raising the temperature of the exhaust gases affect the equilibrium yield of nitrogen in reaction 10.5?

(b) How will raising the temperature and the presence of a catalyst affect the rate of reaction 10.5?

(c) How does the catalyst prevent the formation of nitrogen dioxide? ◀

10.6 Summary of Section 10

1   The rate of a reaction can be defined as the rate at which the concentration of a product increases, or the rate at which the concentration of a reactant decreases.

2   Because molecules must come into contact to react, reactions in solution usually go faster when the concentrations of the reactants are greater, and gaseous reactions usually go faster when the pressure is greater.

3   For all chemical reactions there is an energy barrier. In order for a reaction to occur, reactant molecules must encounter each other with sufficient energy to overcome the barrier.

4   The rate of reaction increases when the temperature increases, because more reactants encounter each other with sufficient energy to overcome the energy barrier.

5   Catalysts increase the rate of a reaction by providing an alternative path with a lower energy barrier. They are not used up during a reaction and do not affect the composition of the equilibrium mixture.

6   The conditions under which a reaction is run are often a compromise between those that will increase the equilibrium yield of a product and those that will increase the rate of the reaction.

Supplying nitrogen for crop production: a case study

11

As a way of drawing together some of the key points from Sections 6–10, we now take a brief look at a practical example of how factors controlling the equilibrium yield and the rate of a reaction affect an important industrial process — the production of nitrogen fertilizers from nitrogen and hydrogen by the Haber–Bosch process.

11.1 Why do crops need nitrogen?

All living things need to take in nitrogen in order to manufacture proteins. The processes by which animals and plants obtain nitrogen are part of an element cycle, the nitrogen cycle. The nitrogen cycle, like the carbon cycle (Block 2), can be subdivided into a geological and a biological cycle, and the part of the cycle that has most effect on crops is the land-based biological cycle. Part of the latter is shown in Figure 11.1.

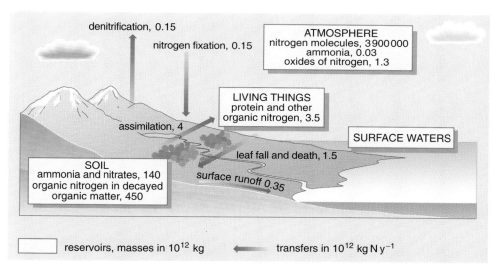

Figure 11.1 Part of the land-based biological nitrogen cycle. Arrows indicate the major transfers of nitrogen. The numbers adjacent to each arrow indicate the mass of nitrogen (N), in the unit of $10^{12}\,\text{kg}\,\text{y}^{-1}$, that is transferred each year world-wide. The chemical forms in which the nitrogen is found, and their masses in the unit of $10^{12}\,\text{kg}$, are indicated in the reservoirs.

● Which is the largest reservoir of nitrogen in the biological cycle?

○ Nitrogen molecules, N_2, in the atmosphere.

Most living organisms cannot use N_2 as their source of nitrogen, and so cannot feed directly off this large reservoir but have to rely on the smaller reservoirs. Plants, for example, take in nitrogen from the soil through their roots, in the form of water-soluble nitrogen-containing compounds, such as sodium nitrate.

Question 11.1   How is this different from the way plants take in carbon in the carbon cycle? ◀

Some nitrogen from the atmosphere is converted into useable forms through the action of bacteria, via a process known as *nitrogen fixation*. The most important of these nitrogen-fixing bacteria, from an agricultural point of view, are those associated with a group of plants known as legumes, that is peas, beans, alfalfa, lentils, lupins, clover and other similar plants. These bacteria invade the roots of these plants

Figure 11.2 Fritz Haber (1868–1934) was awarded the Nobel Prize for Chemistry in 1918 for his work on the synthesis of ammonia. During the First World War, he placed his laboratory at the service of his country, Germany. The work on poisonous gases as weapons carried out in his laboratories during this period led to some French, British and American scientists denouncing his receipt of a Nobel prize. After the war, he developed the Kaiser Wilhelm Institute of physical chemistry and electrochemistry as an international centre.

Figure 11.3 After obtaining his doctorate, Carl Bosch (1874–1940) was given the job of testing a process for converting nitrogen and hydrogen into ammonia. His development of a suitable catalyst and of equipment capable of withstanding the high pressures needed was crucial in enabling ammonia to be produced on an industrial scale. Carl Bosch received the Nobel Prize for Chemistry in 1931.

through the root hairs and form nodules on the roots. They convert nitrogen from the air into ammonia, NH_3, which the plant then uses to make proteins. About 0.15×10^{12} kg of nitrogen are fixed in this way by land-based organisms each year world-wide, but this is only a small fraction of the nitrogen that plants require. The requirements of feeding an increasing human population meant that, around 1900, the fixing of nitrogen by artificial means became a major goal of the chemical industry.

11.2 Using chemistry to fix nitrogen

Various ways of fixing nitrogen from the air were tried in the early 1900s. One method was to mimic the effect of lightning, which can cause atmospheric nitrogen and oxygen to combine to form nitrogen oxides; these oxides dissolve in rain to form nitrates and thus nitrogen reaches the soil. In Britain, rain provides some 10–15 kg of nitrogen per hectare per year for the soil. Next time you are caught out in, or woken up by, a thunderstorm, you may like to reflect that the storm is contributing to the growth of crops by providing essential nitrogen.

The most successful industrial process for fixing nitrogen, which is still in use today, is the **Haber–Bosch process**. This process uses nitrogen (from the air) and hydrogen (produced in a separate process) to manufacture ammonia, NH_3:

$$N_2(g) + 3H_2(g) \rightleftharpoons 2NH_3(g) \qquad (11.1)$$

The high-pressure synthesis of ammonia was first attempted by Henry Le Chatelier (whose fame today lies in Le Chatelier's principle). However, an explosion forced him to abandon the project. Fritz Haber (Figure 11.2) developed the first industrially practicable conditions for the reaction, and Carl Bosch (Figure 11.3) was responsible for the further development of the process to an industrial scale.

11.3 The Haber–Bosch process

Traditionally, the Haber–Bosch process operates at temperatures of 400 °C to 540 °C under high pressure (150–600 times normal atmospheric pressure).

- Look again at Equation 11.1; how does increasing the pressure affect the proportion of ammonia in the equilibrium mixture?

- According to Le Chatelier's principle, to respond to an increase in pressure the composition of the equilibrium mixture will tend to shift in a direction that favours a reduction in the number of gas molecules. There are two moles of product molecules compared with four moles of reactant molecules, and so the increase in pressure will favour the formation of ammonia. There will be a larger proportion of ammonia in the equilibrium mixture.

This is one important reason why industry uses high pressure despite the costs involved. Figure 11.4 shows how the equilibrium yield of ammonia changes with increasing pressure at a fixed temperature of 300 °C.

- The thermochemical equation for the formation of ammonia is:

$$N_2(g) + 3H_2(g) \rightleftharpoons 2NH_3(g) \quad \Delta H = -92.0 \text{ kJ} \qquad (11.2)$$

How will increasing the operating temperature affect the proportion of ammonia in the equilibrium mixture?

○ The reaction is exothermic in the forward direction. Thus, increasing the temperature will *not* favour the formation of ammonia. The proportion of ammonia in the equilibrium mixture will decrease.

Figure 11.5 shows how the equilibrium yield of ammonia changes with increasing temperature at atmospheric pressure and at 100 times atmospheric pressure. In both cases the equilibrium yield of ammonia decreases with increasing temperature.

● Because increasing the temperature decreases the equilibrium yield of ammonia, what other reason must there be for operating the process at relatively high temperatures?

○ Increasing the temperature will increase the rate of reaction. So, operating the process at relatively high temperatures will ensure that ammonia is formed at a practical rate.

As in other industrial processes, the operating conditions selected for the Haber–Bosch process have to take into account *both* the equilibrium yield of the desired product and the rate at which this product is formed. When selecting a suitable operating temperature, the requirements for a high equilibrium yield and a high rate of production are in conflict and a compromise has to be reached. In practice, the process is operated at a high enough temperature to ensure an adequate rate for the production of ammonia. The reaction is also carried out in the presence of a catalyst.

● What role does the catalyst play?

○ It increases the rate of production of ammonia at a given temperature.

The catalyst consists of a mixture of inorganic materials, of which small particles of iron are the main ingredient. When this catalyst is used, a reasonable rate of production of ammonia is achieved at temperatures in the region of 400 °C to 540 °C. In the absence of the catalyst a suitable rate would be achieved only at considerably higher temperatures where, as you can deduce from Figure 11.5, the proportion of ammonia at equilibrium would be low. Even with the catalyst considerable amounts of hydrogen and nitrogen are present in the equilibrium mixture. To avoid wasting these gases, the ammonia is separated out by liquefying it, and the nitrogen and hydrogen are recycled.

The ammonia that is synthesized in the Haber–Bosch process is combined with nitric acid or sulfuric acid to make the solid fertilizers ammonium nitrate, NH_4NO_3, and ammonium sulfate, $(NH_4)_2SO_4$, respectively.

Question 11.2 Natural gas reacts with steam to produce the hydrogen needed for the Haber–Bosch process. The thermochemical equation can be written as follows:

$$CH_4(g) + H_2O(g) \rightleftharpoons CO(g) + 3H_2(g) \quad \Delta H = +206 \, kJ \quad (11.3)$$

The operating conditions are 750 °C and a pressure of 35 atmospheres, and a nickel catalyst is used. Decide whether these conditions increase the yield of hydrogen and/or the rate of reaction, and whether there are any conflicts in realizing both of these aims. ◀

Activity 11.1   Constructing and understanding an argument

Scientists have to think hard about the evidence they gather and what it tells them. In this activity you will be able to think critically about how to use evidence either to support an argument or to uncover a flaw in an argument. ◀

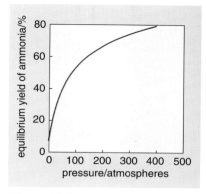

Figure 11.4   The variation in the equilibrium yield of ammonia with increasing pressure at 300 °C. The *initial* mixture contained N_2 and H_2 in molar proportions of 1 : 3. The equilibrium yield of NH_3 is the molar proportion, expressed as a percentage of the total number of moles in the equilibrium mixture.

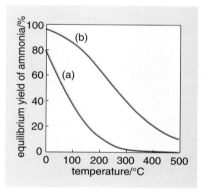

Figure 11.5   The variation in the equilibrium yield of ammonia with increasing temperature at (a) atmospheric pressure and (b) 100 atmospheres. The *initial* mixture contained N_2 and H_2 in molar proportions of 1 : 3. As in Figure 11.4, the equilibrium yield of NH_3 is the molar proportion, expressed as a percentage, in the equilibrium mixture.

11.4 Summary of Section 11

1   Nitrogen is incorporated in different compounds as it moves into and out of living and non-living reservoirs. The largest reservoir of nitrogen is the atmosphere.

2   All living things need a source of nitrogen to produce proteins, but the only living things that can use nitrogen from the atmosphere directly are nitrogen-fixing bacteria.

3   In the Haber–Bosch process, nitrogen gas and hydrogen gas are converted into ammonia gas by passing them over an iron catalyst at high temperature and pressure. The ammonia is converted into solid fertilizers by reaction with nitric or sulfuric acid.

4   The equilibrium yield of ammonia increases with increasing pressure and decreases with increasing temperature.

The chemistry of carbon compounds: crude oil

12

For the remainder of this block we shall examine the properties and reactions of a group of compounds that have carbon as their key building block. It may seem strange to focus on one particular element, but as the carbon cycle, which you met in Block 2, demonstrated, there are a very large number of carbon compounds, many of which are essential to life. Thus, now that we are putting the world back together again, carbon compounds provide the link between atoms and life.

Carbon compounds are also at the heart of perhaps the largest of all industries world-wide, the petrochemical industry. We shall therefore start our study of carbon compounds by looking at crude oil, which is used as a fuel and as a raw material for the production of useful substances. In later sections we shall see how crude oil is broken down into a few simple compounds, which are then used as building blocks to make new compounds such as plastics or pharmaceuticals. We shall continue this study in Block 9, when we examine the chemical compounds that are essential to life.

12.1 A brief history of crude oil

Fossil fuels have been used as a source of energy since ancient times. Coal, the most abundant fossil fuel, provided warmth during the Bronze Age (from 3000 to 2000 BC). Oil and gas were first discovered by the Babylonians and Sumerians, about 2000 BC. In Britain, until the Industrial Revolution the main source of heat was wood or peat. The need for energy to power machinery in the emerging factories meant that coal became the major source of energy, and it continued to dominate until recent times when oil became the major fuel.

The birth of the modern oil industry really dates from the accidental discovery of oil in August 1859 by 'Colonel' Edwin Drake after he had sunk a well near Titusville in Pennsylvania, USA. The potential of this substance was soon realized, and exploration for oil began across North America and then around the world, leading to discoveries of sources in the Middle East, Asia, Eastern Europe and the trans-Caucasus region of the former USSR. Throughout the 20th century the international economic and political importance of crude oil has grown and caused many conflicts, so that now it is a major factor affecting the foreign policy of many countries.

Exploration for oil below the North Sea began in the mid-1960s. Natural gas is usually associated with oil deposits and was found in significant amounts, mainly northeast of the Wash. In 1970 the Norwegian Ekofisk oilfield was discovered farther north. This suggested that the North Sea contained extensive oil resources, a promise that was fulfilled by discoveries of the Forties Field in the British North Sea, also in 1970, and the Brent Field in 1972.

Figure 12.1 shows the global proved reserves of crude oil at the end of 1996.

Figure 12.1 The global proved reserves of crude oil at the end of 1996, measured in 10^9 tonnes. For the UK, the figure was around 0.6×10^9 tonnes, and the annual consumption was around a tenth of this amount.

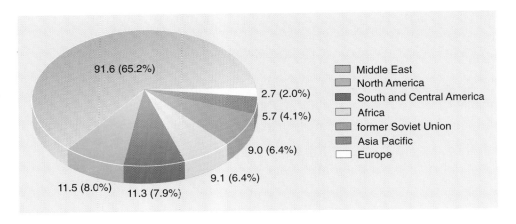

91.6 (65.2%)

2.7 (2.0%)

5.7 (4.1%)

9.0 (6.4%)

9.1 (6.4%)

11.5 (8.0%)   11.3 (7.9%)

☐ Middle East
☐ North America
☐ South and Central America
☐ Africa
☐ former Soviet Union
☐ Asia Pacific
☐ Europe

Figure 12.2 Crude oil is a treacly liquid.

12.2 What is crude oil?

When a pure compound is heated at a particular pressure, it boils at a specific temperature, the boiling temperature. If the gas produced is then cooled, it condenses to give the pure liquid. This is the basis of distillation, which you met in Section 2.2.1 of Block 6. Crude oil, which is a treacly liquid (Figure 12.2), is a mixture containing so many compounds that it boils over a continuous range of temperatures. At the lower temperatures, compounds with a lower boiling temperature vaporize. As the temperature increases, substances with progressively higher boiling temperatures vaporize. Thus, if the crude oil is heated up slowly, the liquid that condenses at the beginning of the distillation will be rich in compounds with low boiling temperatures, whereas the liquid that condenses later will be rich in compounds with high boiling temperatures. By collecting different samples at different times during the distillation we can separate the crude oil into samples that have different ranges of boiling temperatures. Each sample is known as a *fraction* and the complete set of fractions from crude oil is shown in Figure 12.3. However, these fractions are *not* pure compounds; they are still mixtures of many compounds.

Figure 12.3 The fractions obtained by distillation of crude oil. At room temperature, they range from solids (top left) through various liquids to gases (bottom right).

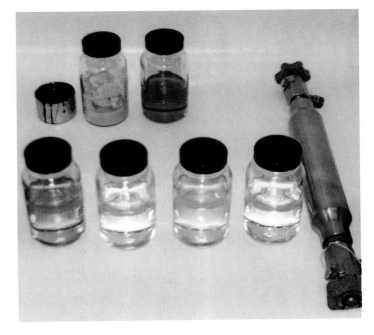

Typical uses of the fractions obtained by industrial distillation are listed below, in ascending order of boiling temperature.

- Gases (boiling temperatures less than 15 °C, about 2% by mass of crude oil) are fuels for burners and electricity generators in refineries. Propane and butane are widely used for heating and cooking in rural communities and for camping stoves, etc.

- Gasoline (boiling range 15–149 °C, about 14% by mass of crude oil) is the raw material for motor car fuel — petrol.

- Kerosene (boiling range 149–232 °C, about 12% by mass of crude oil) is the domestic 'paraffin' and, perhaps surprisingly, is also the main constituent of jet aircraft fuel.

- Diesel (boiling range 232–371 °C, about 21% by mass of crude oil) is the fuel for commercial and domestic vehicles with diesel engines and is also used in domestic central heating systems.

- Lubricating oils (boiling range 371–525 °C, about 19% by mass of crude oil) are used widely for lubricating machinery, such as cars, steam turbine generators and bicycles.

- Waxes (boiling range 371–525 °C, about 2% by mass of crude oil) are used for making candles, impregnating food packaging and electrical insulation.

- Bitumen (boiling temperatures greater than 525 °C, about 30% by mass of crude oil) is used in road surfacing and as a waterproofing agent, particularly in the building industry.

○ The compounds in crude oil contain covalent bonds, that is they exist as discrete molecules. Assuming that the main intermolecular interactions between the molecules in crude oil are London interactions, what can you say about the average relative molecular mass of the various fractions listed above?

○ In Section 7.2 you saw that London interactions between molecules increase with increasing relative molecular mass, and this leads to higher boiling temperatures. This suggests that the higher boiling fractions of crude oil contain larger molecules, which have higher relative molecular masses than the lower boiling fractions.

Despite the fact that there are so many compounds in crude oil, most of them are made up from only carbon and hydrogen atoms. These compounds are collectively known as **hydrocarbons**. How can there be such a rich diversity of compounds made from such simple building blocks?

12.2.1 Linear-chain hydrocarbons

The unique property of carbon that gives it such a rich chemistry is its ability to form chains of atoms of almost any length, to which other atoms can be attached. We'll look at some of these carbon compounds in more detail, but first we need to revisit and extend the chemistry in Section 5.4. There you learnt that carbon invariably forms covalent bonds by sharing electrons with other atoms rather than by forming ions, and that every single bond involves a pair of electrons. We can show this by drawing Lewis structures.

Question 12.1   Carbon has a valency of four and hydrogen a valency of one. What will be the formula of a compound that contains only one carbon and as many hydrogens as are necessary to satisfy the valencies? Draw a Lewis structure of this compound. ◀

To help you to visualize the structures of organic molecules, we have supplied the molecular viewer software WebLab on the CD-ROM for Block 8. Compounds labelled in the text with a superscript W can be viewed by typing in either the name of the compound, e.g. pentane, or the structure number, e.g. **12.1**. You will learn how to use WebLab in Activity 12.2

We can represent the methane[W] molecule in a number of ways. First, there is its molecular formula, CH_4, which tells us only the numbers of each type of atom in the molecule, *not* how the atoms are attached to each other. Secondly we can drawn the Lewis structure, which shows how the outer electrons are shared in the molecule. As we shall see, some molecules involve many such single bonds, and it would be tiresome if we always had to draw out each pair of electrons. Instead, as you saw in Section 4.2.1, a shorthand representation — the structural formula — is used, in which each shared electron pair — a covalent bond — is denoted by a line. The structural formula tells us only which atoms are bonded to which others; it says nothing about the three-dimensional shape of the molecule.

$$CH_4$$

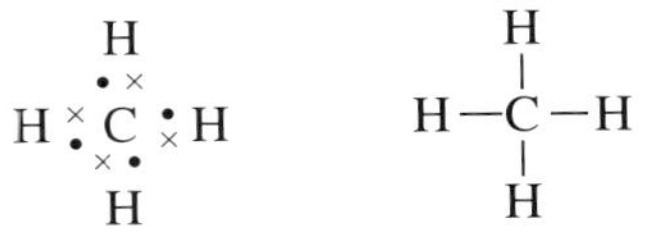

molecular formula   Lewis structure   structural formula

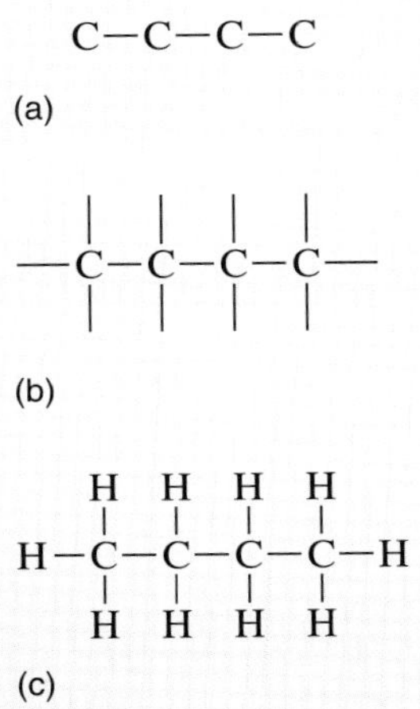

Carbon always forms four bonds. So any structural formula that shows a carbon atom with more or less than four bonds is almost certainly wrong. Put another way, in a structural formula a carbon atom, C, always has four lines (bonds) associated with it.

Butane[W] is another hydrocarbon. It has the molecular formula C_4H_{10} and its molecules consist of a chain of four carbons joined by single bonds, as shown in Figure 12.4a. Each carbon atom needs four bonds, so we can draw in the remaining bonds from each carbon, as shown in Figure 12.4b. Each hydrogen will be attached to the carbon by one bond, so we end up with the structure in Figure 12.4c. Notice that there are ten hydrogen atoms attached to the carbons, in agreement with the molecular formula. Notice also that the chain is created by joining together only carbon atoms; because hydrogen has a valency of one it can never be joined to two other atoms by covalent bonds. In other words, in a structural formula a hydrogen atom, H, always has only one line (bond) associated with it.

Question 12.2   The molecules ethane[W], C_2H_6, and pentane[W], C_5H_{12}, contain linear chains of two and five carbon atoms, respectively. Draw the structural formula for each molecule. ◀

Question 12.3   Propane[W] consists of a chain of three carbon atoms attached to each other by single bonds. It has sufficient hydrogens to satisfy the valency of each carbon. Draw out the structural formula of propane. What is its molecular formula? ◀

Clearly, with long chains of carbon atoms, the structural formulae will soon get very cumbersome. We can simplify things by using an **abbreviated structural formula**. Here only the bonds between the carbon atoms are drawn and not the bonds to the hydrogen atoms. The number of hydrogens on each carbon (which are needed to satisfy the valency of 4) is shown using the hydrogen symbol, H, with a subscript. For example, butane (Figure 12.4c) is represented as CH_3—CH_2—CH_2—CH_3. Note that the bonds shown in the abbreviated structural formula are the carbon-to-carbon bonds; they do not link the hydrogens to the carbons.

Methane, ethane, propane, butane and pentane are called linear-chain hydrocarbons, because each carbon atom is bonded to a maximum of two other carbon atoms, giving

(a)

(b)

(c)

Figure 12.4   Three stages in drawing the structural formula of butane.

the appearance of a linear chain of carbon atoms when the structural formula is written down. Crude oil contains many different linear-chain hydrocarbons: every one from methane to $C_{78}H_{158}$ has been found in crude oil.

Throughout the rest of this block you will meet many new compounds. These will be referred to either by a name or by a structure numbered in bold type, such as **12.1**. As we shall see in a moment, the naming of carbon compounds can get quite complex, but you do not need to learn or even understand the names of such compounds. If you are worried by the names, just think of them as labels. Similarly it is not necessary for you to remember particular structures; when a structure is needed you will always be given it.

Activity 12.1 Identifying patterns in structural formulae

In this activity you will examine a number of linear-chain hydrocarbons and the ways in which they can be represented. ◀

12.2.2 Branched-chain hydrocarbons

Another type of hydrocarbon found in crude oil is the branched-chain hydrocarbon. Most of the compounds in this category have molecules that have a chain of carbon atoms with a 'branch' of one carbon atom on the side, as shown in Table 12.1. Depending on its position in the chain, the one carbon atom branch can be represented in various ways:

$$CH_3 \quad | \qquad CH_3{-} \qquad {-}CH_3$$
$$| \qquad CH_3$$

All these forms mean the same thing, a carbon atom with three hydrogens attached; the carbon is also bonded to another carbon atom in a hydrocarbon molecule. $CH_3{-}$ is known as a **methyl group** because it is like *meth*ane but has one bond to another carbon instead of a fourth hydrogen.

As you progress through this section we will sometimes refer to groups such as $CH_3{-}$ or ${-}CH_2{-}$, where there are 'dangling bonds', at one or both ends of the group, which do not seem to be attached to other atoms. These are not separate molecules, but represent *parts* of a molecule, and it is assumed that in a molecule they are attached to other atoms. For example, in $CH_3{-}CH_2{-}CH_3$, we can identify one ${-}CH_2{-}$ and two $CH_3{-}$ groups.

Notice from Table 12.1 that the molecular formula of 2-methylpropane, C_4H_{10}, is the same as that of butane (Figure 12.4). However, their boiling temperatures are different (butane boils at 0 °C). Different compounds that have the same molecular formula are called **isomers**. This chemical individuality results from the same atoms being joined together in different ways to give different molecules. In this case, butane involves a chain of four carbon atoms whereas 2-methylpropane has a chain of three carbon atoms and a branch of one carbon atom — a methyl group. With Lego or some other building set, given a particular number of building blocks you can usually construct a range of different structures. So it is with the chemical building blocks — atoms. We can arrange the same set of atoms in different ways. For example, remembering that each carbon needs to have four bonds attached and each hydrogen

Table 12.1 The names, formulae and boiling temperatures of some branched-chain hydrocarbons.

Name	Molecular formula	Structural formula	Abbreviated structural formula	Boiling temperature/°C
2-methylpropane[W]	C_4H_{10}		$CH_3-CH-CH_3$ $\quad\quad\ \ CH_3$	−12
2-methylbutane[W]	C_5H_{12}		$CH_3-CH-CH_2-CH_3$ $\quad\quad\ \ CH_3$	28
2-methylpentane[W]	C_6H_{14}		$CH_3-CH-CH_2-CH_2-CH_3$ $\quad\quad\ \ CH_3$	60

one bond attached, there are three ways in which we can order five carbon atoms and twelve hydrogen atoms, as shown in structures **12.1**[W], **12.2**[W] and **12.3**[W]. These all have the same molecular formula, C_5H_{12}, but different boiling temperatures: 36 °C, 28 °C and 10 °C, respectively.

12.1   **12.2**   **12.3**

What are the molecular formulae of structures **12.4**, **12.5** and **12.6**?

12.4   **12.5**   **12.6**

All three structures have five carbon atoms and twelve hydrogen atoms, so they all have the molecular formula C_5H_{12}.

At first sight you may think that structures **12.4**, **12.5** and **12.6** represent different compounds. After all, the structural formulae certainly look very different. In fact, they are all the same linear-chain hydrocarbon. Remember that the structural formula says nothing about the *shape* of the molecule; it tells us only the order in which atoms are bonded together. If you compare the structures you will see that each has a chain of five carbon atoms with three hydrogen atoms attached to each of the carbon atoms at the ends and two hydrogen atoms attached to each of the three carbon atoms in the middle. They have simply been drawn out differently.

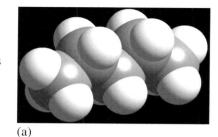
(a)

● Is structure **12.1** the same compound as that represented by structures **12.4–12.6**?

○ Yes. Structure **12.1** has the molecular formula C_5H_{12}. It also has a chain of five carbon atoms with three hydrogen atoms attached to each of the carbon atoms at the ends and two hydrogen atoms attached to each of the three carbon atoms in the middle.

Structures **12.4–12.6** are folded representations of **12.1** and if you were to pull them out, like you would a folded piece of string, you would get the linear form, **12.1**.

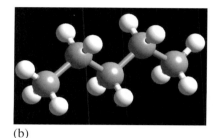
(b)

Figure 12.5   (a) Space-filling representation and (b) ball-and-stick representation of the linear-chain form of C_5H_{12}.

Structures such as **12.4–12.6** look like different molecules at first, because when we draw a structural formula on a page we represent the molecule in two dimensions. However, atoms and molecules exist in a three-dimensional world. Our two-dimensional representations of structural formulae do not show the shape, and so we need a three-dimensional representation. There are several types of such representation. Two of the most important are space-filling representations (Figure 12.5a) and ball-and-stick representations (Figure 12.5b). These are both used in the WebLab software.

Activity 12.2 The shapes of molecules

This CD-ROM activity gives you practice in drawing structural formulae in two dimensions. It also introduces you to the WebLab molecular viewer. ◀

12.2.3 What else is in crude oil?

In science, one of the ways of making sense of many different things is to classify them — organize them into groups that have similar features. We used this approach in Block 3 with rocks, in Block 4 with organisms and in Block 6 with elements and the Periodic Table. Figure 12.6 shows one way of classifying most of the thousands of compounds in crude oil.

Most of the compounds are hydrocarbons, and we can divide these into two groups: alkanes and aromatics. In **alkanes**, the carbon atoms are joined by *single* bonds. (As you will see in a moment there are other examples of hydrocarbons where the carbons are joined by double bonds.) Alkanes comprise a **class of compounds**. In this context, a class of compounds contains compounds with similar chemical structures and similar elemental compositions. So far, you have learnt that crude oil contains the sub-classes of linear-chain hydrocarbons and branched-chain hydrocarbons, or more precisely **linear-chain alkanes** and **branched-chain alkanes**. Another sub-class of alkanes in crude oil is the **cycloalkanes**. As the name implies, cycloalkanes are alkanes whose structures involve carbon atoms joined in a ring (cycle) by single bonds, for example cyclohexane (**12.7**)^W and cyclopentane (**12.8**)^W , so each carbon is bonded to two other carbons and to two hydrogens.

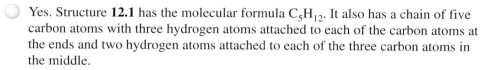

         12.7   12.8

Figure 12.6 A classification of the compounds in crude oil. Oil from different sources has different compositions, so the percentages are shown here as ranges.

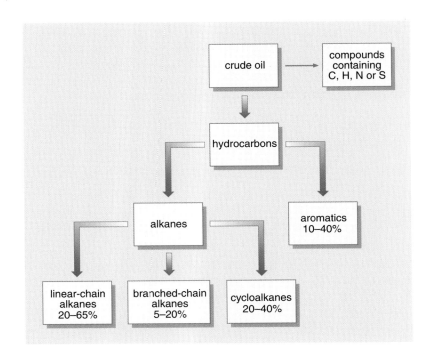

Question 12.4 Classify the structures **12.9**[W], **12.10**[W], **12.11**[W] and **12.12**[W] as a linear-chain alkane, a branched-chain alkane, a cycloalkane or a compound that is not an alkane. ◀

12.9

12.10

12.11

12.12

The other class of hydrocarbons present in crude oil is the **aromatic compounds**. These are compounds that have a characteristic group in which six carbon atoms are joined in a ring by alternating single and double bonds, with only one other atom bonded to each carbon atom. The simplest aromatic compound is benzene[W] (**12.13**).

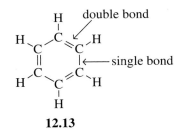

12.13

- Are the valencies of all the atoms satisfied in benzene?

- Yes, each of the hydrogen atoms is attached by one bond and each of the carbon atoms has four bonds — two single bonds and one double bond.

- Why isn't benzene an alkane?

- Alkanes are compounds that contain only carbon and hydrogen, with the carbons joined by *single* bonds. In benzene some of the carbons are joined by double bonds.

As Figure 12.6 shows, crude oils also contain small amounts of compounds that are not hydrocarbons, because they contain sulfur and/or nitrogen as well as carbon and hydrogen. They too can be divided into sub-classes, some of which we shall meet later.

12.2.4 The names of organic compounds

We shall finish this section with a few comments on the names of the compounds you will meet in the remaining sections. There are two ways of naming compounds. The first is an older system that often reflects the first source of the compound, for example, citric acid was originally obtained from citrus fruits. The second involves a systematic nomenclature and is based on a universally agreed system. Any experienced chemist reading the systematic name would be able to work out its structural formula. For example, the compounds in Table 12.1 were all called 2-methyl something. This means that the second carbon of the main hydrocarbon chain (in this case propane, butane or pentane) has a methyl group attached to it. However, the names can get very complex. For example, citric acid, a relatively simple compound, has the systematic name 2-hydroxy-1,2,3-propanetricarboxylic acid! One method is neat, but doesn't tell you much about its structure, whereas the other is precise but very unwieldy. Either way you are not expected to learn the names. In general we shall use the systematic name, except when the older name is in general use, when we put the systematic name in brackets.

Question 12.5   Identify the classes, and sub-classes where appropriate, of the compounds **12.14**^{W}, **12.15**^{W}, **12.16**^{W} and **12.17**^{W}. ◄

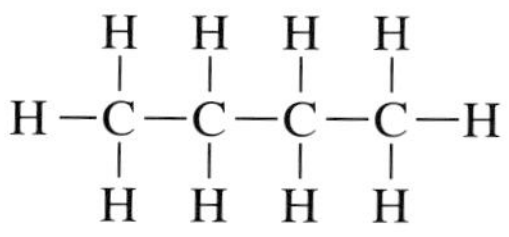

12.14

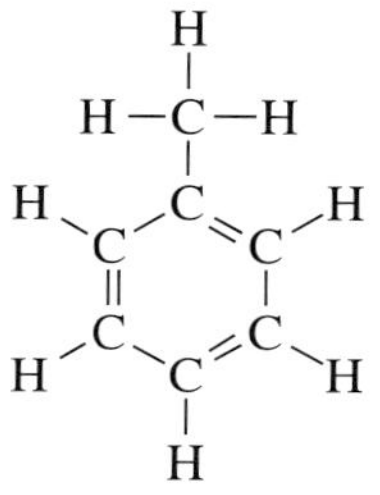

12.15

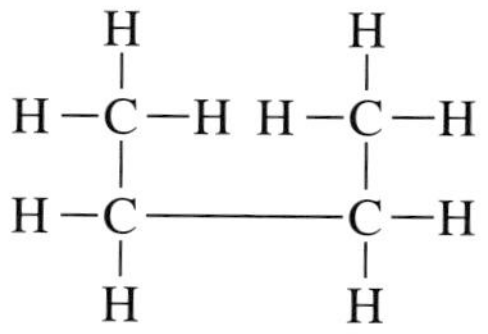

12.16

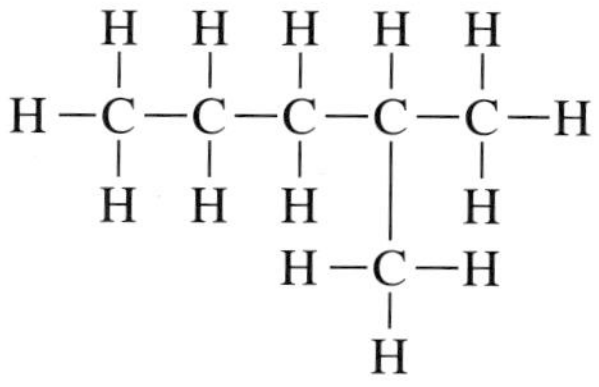

12.17

Question 12.6   Which one of the alkanes **12.18**^{W}, **12.19**^{W} and **12.20**^{W}does not have a correct structural formula in which all the valencies are satisfied? ◄

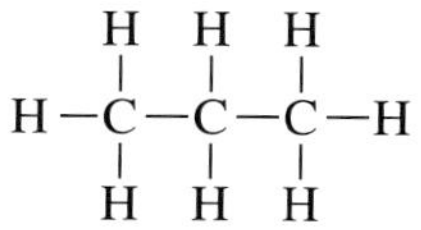

12.18

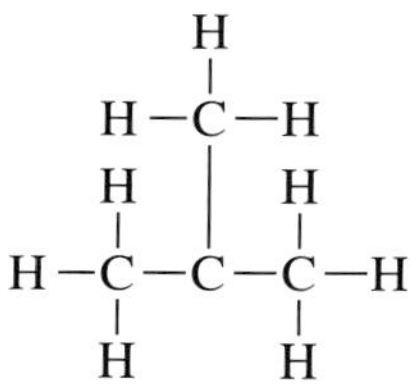

12.19

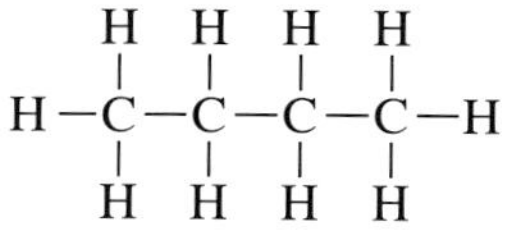

12.20

Question 12.7 Without looking back, draw out the structural formulae and the abbreviated structural formulae for the following: (a) the linear-chain alkane C_8H_{18}; (b) the cycloalkane C_4H_8, which contains a ring of four carbon atoms; (c) the branched-chain alkane C_4H_{10}; (d) the cycloalkane C_5H_{10}, which contains a ring of four carbon atoms. ◄

12.3 Oil as a fuel: petrol

In this section we examine how oil is used as a fuel. To illustrate this we concentrate on petrol (or, as it is known in the USA, gasoline), the most familiar of the fuel fractions. The gasoline fraction from the distillation of crude oil consists mainly of linear-chain alkanes containing between six and ten carbon atoms. The combustion of octane[W], C_8H_{18}, is typical of the combustion reaction of petrol:

$$2C_8H_{18}(g) + 25O_2(g) \longrightarrow 16CO_2(g) + 18H_2O(g)$$

⬤ One litre of octane has a mass of about 800 grams. Using data from Table 6.1, calculate how much energy is released when a litre of octane is burnt.

◯ From Table 6.1, the energy released from a kilogram of octane is 45 000 kJ. Because a litre of octane has a mass of about 0.8 kg, the energy released when one litre is burnt is:

$$45\,000\,\text{kJ kg}^{-1} \times 0.8\,\text{kg} = 36\,000\,\text{kJ}$$

The gasoline fraction from crude oil is rather poor as a fuel for the modern internal combustion engine. The engine doesn't run smoothly, a phenomenon known as 'knocking'. Different sub-classes of alkanes vary in the amount of knocking they cause when they burn: linear-chain alkanes cause more knocking than the other sub-classes.

The extent of the knocking caused by a fuel is expressed as its **octane number** (or Research Octane Number, RON). The values are equivalent to the percentage (by volume) of *iso*-octane (2,2,4-trimethylpentane) (**12.21**)[W] in a mixture of *iso*-octane and heptane (**12.22**)[W] that has the same extent of knocking as the fuel. So, for example, because cyclohexane causes the same amount of knocking as a mixture of 83% *iso*-octane and 17% heptane, its octane number is 83. Some sample values are listed in Table 12.2.

The different grades of the petrol that is put into cars have slightly different compositions, and thus different octane numbers. The latter are shown on the pumps at filling stations – 95 for 'premium' grades and 98 for 'super' grades. The higher the octane number, the better the fuel performs.

12.21   12.22

Table 12.2 Some typical octane numbers.

Octane number	Sub-class	Compound
0	linear-chain alkane	heptane
25	linear-chain alkane	hexane
42	branched-chain alkane	2-methylhexane
83	cycloalkane	cyclohexane
93	branched-chain alkane	2,2-dimethylpentane
100	branched-chain alkane	*iso*-octane
106	aromatic	benzene
111	aromatic	toluene

One way of improving the octane number is to add tetraethyl-lead, which acts as an anti-knock agent. Adding 0.6 g of tetraethyl-lead to one litre of a fuel can improve the octane number by between 5 and 10. Concern about the hazard to health from lead in the atmosphere has meant that the use of 'leaded' petrol has been discouraged in many countries, and it is likely to be phased out entirely. However, unleaded fuels cause other problems: in order to achieve an acceptable octane number, high proportions of aromatic compounds are often added to a fuel, and some of these are quite toxic.

Compounds that are suitable for motor fuel make up only 20% by mass of crude oil. The fractions containing bigger molecules, such as the lubricating oils, are too viscous, and have too high a boiling temperature, so they do not burn efficiently in an internal combustion engine. However, the compounds in the other fractions can be converted into compounds that are more suitable for motor fuel. In most refineries the crude oil is first distilled to give a range of fractions, then each fraction undergoes a different treatment. For example, if the high-boiling fractions are heated in the presence of a catalyst, the larger molecules 'crack' into smaller hydrocarbons.

⬤ Suppose the molecule $C_{16}H_{34}$ is cracked into two smaller molecules, C_8H_{18}:

$$C_{16}H_{34}(g) + ? \longrightarrow 2C_8H_{18}(g)$$

What is needed to balance the equation?

◯ Both sides have 16 carbon atoms, but whereas the right-hand side has 36 hydrogen atoms (2×18), the left-hand side has only 34. Thus, hydrogen, H_2, is needed on the left-hand side to balance the equation.

When any hydrocarbon is broken down into smaller fragments, hydrogen needs to be supplied if linear-chain or branched-chain alkanes are to be obtained. This process is called **hydrocracking**, in which the atoms are rearranged to give a mixture of mainly branched-chain alkanes. This produces a more suitable motor fuel, not only because the molecules are shorter, but also because, as Table 12.2 shows, branching means that the fuel has a higher octane number.

Modern hydrocracking processes use catalysts, known as zeolites, which contain aluminium, silicon and oxygen, at temperatures around 500 °C.

● Why is a catalyst used?

○ In Section 10, you learned that a catalyst is employed to speed up a reaction. It provides the reaction with an alternative reaction pathway involving a lower energy barrier. It does not alter the position of the equilibrium. In the absence of a catalyst, higher temperatures and pressures would be necessary.

Even with a catalyst, pressures of up to 200 atmospheres are still necessary to obtain acceptable conversions, which means that the reaction vessels need to be very strong — their walls are often 15–20 cm thick and their design and construction pose many difficult engineering problems. Hydrocracking is a continuous process, in that reactants go in one end and react together, and the products are then separated and isolated at the other end.

Another process that is important in the production of petrol is **catalytic reforming**. This involves converting linear-chain alkanes into aromatic compounds, cycloalkanes and branched-chain alkanes.

● What is the advantage, for the production of petrol, of forming such compounds?

○ Table 12.2 shows that aromatic compounds, cycloalkanes and branched-chain alkanes have higher octane numbers than linear-chain alkanes.

A typical process is the conversion of heptane into toluene (methylbenzene[W]):

Notice that one of the products is hydrogen, which can then be used in hydrocracking. Again a catalyst is employed to speed up the process.

Processes such as hydrocracking and catalytic reforming are used to treat the various fractions obtained by distillation of crude oil so that when the products are mixed together a high performance petrol with a high octane number is produced, which meets the demands of the modern car. Table 12.3 shows the composition of a typical mixture.

Table 12.3 The proportions of different hydrocarbons used in petrol.

Compound	Proportion
butane	10%
other alkanes	60–65%
aromatics	25–30%

12.4 Summary of Section 12

1 Crude oil is a mixture of hydrocarbons, mainly alkanes and aromatic compounds, together with small amounts of compounds containing sulfur and/or nitrogen. The sub-classes of alkanes are linear-chain, branched-chain and cycloalkanes.

2 Crude oil contains so many different hydrocarbons that individual compounds cannot be easily isolated. However, it can be separated into different fractions on the basis of their boiling temperatures. Each fraction has different uses.

3 Because carbon readily forms bonds to other carbon atoms, chains of carbon atoms form with sufficient hydrogen atoms to satisfy the valency of carbon. Such molecules can be represented using structural formulae and abbreviated structural formulae.

4   Different compounds that have the same molecular formula are known as isomers.

5   Three-dimensional representations are much better for visualizing molecules.

6   The octane number of a fuel reflects how much knocking it causes. The higher the octane number, the better the fuel performs. The gasoline fraction of crude oil is mainly linear-chain alkanes, and the addition of branched-chain alkanes, aromatic compounds or tetraethyl-lead improves the octane number.

7   The gasoline fraction of crude oil is supplemented by the manufacture of branched-chain alkanes from larger molecules using the process of hydrocracking. Catalytic reforming involves the formation of aromatic compounds that can be used to increase the octane number.

Question 12.8   Another process used in refineries is known as isomerization. It converts pentane and hexane, which are linear-chain alkanes, into compounds with higher octane numbers. Write out one typical reaction for hexane (**12.23**)^W — the name of the process gives you the clue. ◀

$$CH_3-CH_2-CH_2-CH_2-CH_2-CH_3$$

12.23

13 What else is oil used for?

Section 12 described crude oil and some of its uses as a fuel, but is this the only reason why crude oil is so important — to burn? In one year in the UK, about nine million tonnes of crude oil are converted into materials that end up as plastics, pesticides, drugs, adhesives, paints, solvents and so on — materials referred to collectively as petrochemicals. This is because crude oil is a source of carbon compounds that can be readily transformed into these useful products. However, only 11% of crude oil is used to make other chemicals; 89% is burnt for fuel. There is always controversy about the use of coal and crude oil derivatives as fuels rather than for what the petrochemical industry refers to as their 'more noble use' as raw materials (feedstocks) for the manufacturing and petrochemical industries (see Box 13.1, *The chemical industry*). This is by no means a recent concern; as early as 1872 Mendeléev (the Russian chemist who devised the Periodic Table that you studied in Block 6) is said to have reported to his government that oil was too valuable a resource to be burned and should be preserved as a source of chemicals.

Box 13.1 The chemical industry

The UK chemical industry is the country's largest exporter and the fourth largest manufacturing industry, after food, drink and tobacco, mechanical engineering, and printing and publishing. The sizes of the various sectors of the chemical industry, based on revenue, are shown in Figure 13.1. Petrochemicals are involved in one way or another in most of these sectors.

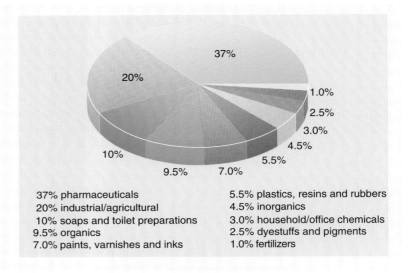

37% pharmaceuticals
20% industrial/agricultural
10% soaps and toilet preparations
9.5% organics
7.0% paints, varnishes and inks

5.5% plastics, resins and rubbers
4.5% inorganics
3.0% household/office chemicals
2.5% dyestuffs and pigments
1.0% fertilizers

Figure 13.1 The sizes of the sectors of the chemical industry, based on revenue.

The development of petrochemicals has revolutionized our lives (see title page). All these changes, and many more, have been brought about through the discovery and exploitation of the chemical and physical properties of carbon compounds. Carbon chemistry can be regarded as 'designer chemistry' in a literal sense. Petrochemicals have not just appeared as a result of the discovery of crude oil, but have required the ingenuity of chemists to build new molecules. The properties of a compound are related to its molecular structure, and, as we shall see, by designing particular features into molecules we can dictate their properties. For example, we can make a drug that acts on only one part of the body, or a plastic that is as strong as steel.

However, as well as improving the quality of life for many millions of people, some of these developments have had adverse consequences. Some medicines, such as thalidomide, had unforeseen side effects. The use of CFCs as refrigerants and propellants has created a potentially long-term problem by damaging the ozone layer around the Earth. Some pesticides, such as DDT, have had a detrimental impact on wildlife. However, chemistry is no worse than other areas of human endeavour — all have their positive and negative aspects. Nevertheless, for better or for worse, modern life, particularly in developed countries, relies heavily on the chemistry of industrially produced carbon compounds.

Naturally occurring carbon compounds are also very important because the existence of life is based on carbon chemistry. As you will see in Block 9, all living things on this planet rely on the reactions and products of an incredible variety of complex carbon compounds. It was because carbon compounds were produced from living organisms that this branch of chemistry became known as **organic chemistry**, a name it retains today, even though many of the new compounds have nothing to do with organisms. The branch of chemistry associated with compounds that do not contain carbon is known as **inorganic chemistry**. Even though organic chemistry is based on only a few elements of the Periodic Table, over 90% of all known chemical compounds are organic compounds! This is due to the unique ability of carbon to form bonds with other carbon atoms to give chains of almost any length and shape.

When we build a model using Lego we use building blocks that can be joined together. In the same way, when we build organic molecules we use building blocks made up of one or more atoms that can be joined together using chemical reactions. We shall now investigate how crude oil supplies the building blocks to create products such as drugs, detergents, plastics, paints and vitamins. We shall also examine the relatively small number of reactions that allow us to join these building blocks together.

13.1 Important chemical feedstocks

Crude oil is mainly made up of alkanes, but unfortunately, such compounds are not particularly adaptable starting materials for the chemical industry. This is because, apart from combustion, alkanes are essentially unreactive and any reactions they do undergo are fairly uncontrollable. Instead, the compounds in crude oil need to be converted into more reactive compounds and also into relatively small molecules, for versatility.

If alkanes are heated strongly *without added hydrogen gas*, smaller, more useful compounds are produced. This process is called *cracking*, because larger molecules are 'cracked' up into smaller molecules. A typical transformation for cracking is:

$$CH_3-CH_2-CH_2-CH_2-CH_2-CH_2-CH_2-CH_2-CH_3 \ (g)$$

$$\downarrow$$

$$H_2(g) \ + \ CH_2{=}CH_2 \ (g) \ + \ CH_3-CH{=}CH_2 \ (g) \ + \ CH_3-CH_2-CH{=}CH_2 \ (g) \ \text{------}$$

Most of the compounds produced by cracking contain the unit $C{=}C$, because without added hydrogen gas there are not enough hydrogen atoms available to satisfy all the valencies of carbon.

⬤ Draw the Lewis structure of $CH_2{=}CH_2$. What do we mean by a $C{=}C$ unit?

◯ You met double bonds when we discussed the bonding in carbon dioxide, $O{=}C{=}O$, in Section 5. Structure **13.1** shows the Lewis structure of $CH_2{=}CH_2$, which is called *ethene*. There are four electrons between the two carbons, indicating *two* separate two-electron bonds, usually called a double bond. Thus, a $C{=}C$ unit indicates the presence of a double bond.

13.1

Alkanes have four atoms around each carbon atom all attached by single bonds and are called **saturated compounds**. Compounds that contain a $C{=}C$ unit have only three atoms around each of these carbons because these two carbon atoms are attached to each other by a double bond. Such compounds are called **unsaturated compounds**. You may have met the term 'polyunsaturates', in connection with margarines; this merely means that the molecules that make up the oil or fat in the margarine contain more than one carbon–carbon double bond. The class of hydrocarbons that contain a C=C unit are called **alkenes** and some examples are given in Table 13.1. Notice the subtle and often missed difference of one letter between alkanes, saturated hydrocarbons, and alkenes, unsaturated hydrocarbons. As you will see, the alkene double bond provides an excellent site for chemical transformation, because the carbon–carbon double bond reacts readily and in a controllable fashion. However, before we examine the reactivity of alkenes, let's look more closely at how these versatile compounds are produced from crude oil.

Table 13.1   Some typical alkenes.

Name	Molecular structure
ethene[W]	$CH_2{=}CH_2$
propene[W]	$CH_2{=}CH{-}CH_3$
but-1-ene[W]	$CH_2{=}CH{-}CH_2{-}CH_3$
but-2-ene[W]	$CH_3{-}CH{=}CH{-}CH_3$
buta-1,3-diene[W]	$CH_2{=}CH{-}CH{=}CH_2$
2-methylpropene[W]	$CH_2{=}C{\overset{\diagup CH_3}{\diagdown CH_3}}$

The simple alkenes are generally made by a cracking process called **catalytic cracking**. One of the higher boiling fractions of crude oil is heated to about 350 °C and then passed over a zeolite catalyst. By adjusting temperature, pressure and contact time with the catalyst, the nature of the reaction products can be controlled quite precisely. Although we start with a mixture containing thousands of different compounds, the molecules 'crack' up to give a mixture of the same small molecules, usually about five or six alkenes. The products from a typical catalytic cracker are the alkenes in Table 13.1.

Activity 13.1 Summarizing chemical processes

This activity develops your skill at summarizing chemical processes. ◀

Each of the alkenes formed by catalytic cracking finds extensive use as a raw material in laboratory and industrial chemistry. They are good building blocks because they are small molecules and are reactive. In particular they can undergo what are known as **addition reactions**[*], as shown below:

$$X{-}Y + CH_2{=}CH_2 \longrightarrow X{-}CH_2{-}CH_2{-}Y$$

Effectively, the hypothetical molecule X—Y, where both X and Y are atoms or groups of atoms, is incorporated in (added to) the alkene. One of the bonds in the double bond between the carbons is broken, and in the product one of the carbon atoms now forms a bond to X and the other forms a bond to Y. We say that X and Y have been *added across* the double bond. Addition reactions are one of the six key types of reaction that are described in this block, and listed in Appendix 1 of the Study File for Block 8. Typical addition reactions of ethene are:

$$CH_2{=}CH_2 \;+\; H_2 \longrightarrow \overset{\displaystyle H \quad\; H}{\underset{\textstyle CH_2{-}CH_2}{\displaystyle |\quad\;\; |}} \tag{13.1}$$

This product can also be written as $CH_3{-}CH_3$.

[*]So that you can concentrate on the change taking place, the state symbols (s), (g), (l) and (aq) will not be used for this and subsequent equations.

$$CH_2{=}CH_2 \; + \; Br_2 \; \longrightarrow \; \begin{matrix} Br & Br \\ | & | \\ CH_2 & {-} & CH_2 \end{matrix} \qquad (13.2)$$

This product can also be written as $Br{-}CH_2{-}CH_2{-}Br$.

$$CH_2{=}CH_2 \; + \; H_2O \; \longrightarrow \; \begin{matrix} H & OH \\ | & | \\ CH_2 & {-} & CH_2 \end{matrix} \qquad (13.3)$$

This product can also be written as $CH_3{-}CH_2{-}OH$.

All these cases involve the addition of extra atoms or groups to the reactant to form new single bonds.

⬤ Identify X and Y in Equations 13.1 to 13.3.

◯ In Equation 13.1, hydrogen is added across the double bond. We can write hydrogen as $H{-}H$, so both X and Y are H. In Equation 13.2, bromine is added across the double bond. We can write bromine as $Br{-}Br$, so both X and Y are Br. In Equation 13.3, water, H_2O, is added across the double bond. We can write water as $H{-}OH$, so X is H and Y is OH.

Other alkenes in Table 13.1 react with bromine in a similar fashion:

$$CH_3{-}CH{=}CH_2 \; + \; Br_2 \; \longrightarrow \; \begin{matrix} Br \\ | \\ CH_3{-}CH{-}CH_2{-}Br \end{matrix} \qquad (13.4)$$

$$CH_3{-}CH{=}CH{-}CH_3 \; + \; Br_2 \; \longrightarrow \; \begin{matrix} Br & Br \\ | & | \\ CH_3{-}CH{-}CH{-}CH_3 \end{matrix} \qquad (13.5)$$

So, by converting crude oil into a mixture of just a few alkenes, we have a suitable feedstock that readily undergoes conversion into other compounds. As we shall see, these compounds can themselves undergo further transformations, leading to a wide range of petrochemical products.

⬤ Draw the reaction between but-1-ene, $CH_3{-}CH_2{-}CH{=}CH_2$, and hydrogen, H_2.

◯ $$CH_3{-}CH_2{-}CH{=}CH_2 \; + \; H_2 \; \longrightarrow \; \begin{matrix} H & H \\ | & | \\ CH_3{-}CH_2{-}CH{-}CH_2 \end{matrix}$$

In answering this question you have used a strategy that is probably the most important in organic chemistry — the functional group approach. You have to reason that the saturated alkane part of the molecule, $CH_3{-}CH_2{-}$, is unreactive, and hydrogen reacts only with the double bond in a reaction similar to Equation 13.1. This reasoning follows the pattern of reactivity demonstrated in the addition of bromine to different alkenes (Equations 13.2, 13.4 and 13.5). The functional group approach is the topic of the next section.

13.2 Summary of Section 13

1 The complex mixture of alkanes in crude oil is converted into five or six alkenes (compounds that contain carbon–carbon double bonds) by catalytic cracking.

2 The alkenes obtained from crude oil are small molecules that are reactive and undergo addition reactions, enabling them to be converted into other useful compounds.

14 Functional groups and their reactions

14.1 The functional group approach

We'll start our discussion of functional groups with a brief overview provided on CD-ROM.

Activity 14.1 An introduction to functional groups

In this activity you will look at the functional group approach and how it helps us to predict the properties and reactivities of organic compounds. ◀

As you saw in Activity 14.1, the **functional group approach** helps us to make sense of the mass of data available on the thirteen million or so known organic compounds. It enables us to examine the structure of a molecule and to predict and understand its chemical reactivity and its physical properties. Essentially, we assume that only certain parts of a molecule contribute to its reactivity. This is an oversimplification because reactivity is determined by the structure of the whole molecule, but to a first approximation it works surprisingly well. We can regard organic molecules as having two distinct parts: the **functional group** or groups, and the rest of the molecule. The reason for this is that when organic compounds react *only the functional group undergoes chemical change*. The functional groups are relatively easy to spot because they usually involve atoms other than carbon and hydrogen, such as oxygen and nitrogen; alkenes are one of the few exceptions. Remember, the molecules are not physically broken up into functional groups and the rest of the molecule; this is simply an imaginary distinction that helps us to make sense of their reactivity.

Functional groups are also used as a means of classifying organic compounds. All the compounds in Table 13.1 are alkenes because they all contain a carbon–carbon double-bond functional group, which can undergo addition reactions. From now on, we shall highlight functional groups with a tinted background. Thus the first two of the alkenes in Table 13.1 can be represented as structures **14.1**^{W} and **14.2**^{W}.

The classes of organic compounds that you will meet most frequently in this course are shown in Appendix 1 in the Study File for Block 8, together with their characteristic functional groups. These functional groups will come up again and again in the rest of this block so it is important that you have Appendix 1 at hand to help you to recognize them.

When drawing structural formulae of organic compounds it is essential to ensure that the number of bonds to each type of atom reflects the valencies of the atoms. The functional groups we shall meet contain the elements carbon, hydrogen, nitrogen, oxygen and the halogens, and their valencies are given in Table 14.1.

We shall now look at some of these functional groups in more detail to illustrate the strength of the functional group approach.

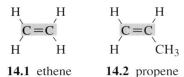

14.1 ethene   **14.2** propene

Table 14.1 The valencies of some common elements found in functional groups.

Element	Valency
hydrogen	1
carbon	4
nitrogen	3
oxygen	2
fluorine	1
chlorine	1
bromine	1
iodine	1

14.1.1 Haloalkanes

The haloalkanes are a class of compounds that contain one or more halogen atoms as well as carbon and hydrogen atoms. They contain one or more of the functional groups —F, —Cl, —Br and —I.

⬤ Write down the molecular formula and the Lewis structure of fluoromethane, which contains one fluorine atom, one carbon atom and sufficient hydrogen atoms to satisfy the valency of the carbon.

◯ Fluorine has the shell structure (2,7), with seven outer electrons. It can attain the shell structure of the noble gas neon (2,8) by gaining one electron from one electron pair. This means that fluorine forms only one covalent bond — it has a valency of one — so three hydrogens are needed to satisfy the valency of carbon. The molecular formula of fluoromethane is CH_3F, and its Lewis structure is shown in the margin.

You may have written the molecular formula as FH_3C, H_3CF or H_3FC, which are all reasonable answers, but chemists have a convention that:

> The molecular formula of an organic compound is always written with the symbol for the carbon atoms first, then the symbol for the hydrogen atoms, followed by the symbols for any other elements, in alphabetical order.

The Lewis structure of fluoromethane shows that the carbon–fluorine bond involves two electrons, and that there are six other electrons around the fluorine, which form three unshared, or **non-bonded**, **electron pairs**. When the bonding electron pairs are replaced by lines in the structural formula, these non-bonded electron pairs are usually left out, as shown in structure **14.3**[W].

14.3

All the halogens have a valency of one, which enables us to predict the formulae of the compounds they form with carbon.

⬤ Write down the molecular formulae of all the compounds that contain one carbon atom and as many chlorine atoms, or hydrogen atoms, or mixtures of the two, as are required for the valency of carbon to be satisfied.

◯ Hydrogen and chlorine both have a valency of one, so we can attach four of these atoms in any combination to the carbon atom. There are five such compounds: CH_4, CH_3Cl, CH_2Cl_2, $CHCl_3$, CCl_4. (Note that these formulae are written to conform with the convention above.)

CCl_4 is known as tetrachloromethane (carbon tetrachloride). It was formerly used as a solvent for removing stains in proprietary products such as 'Dabitoff'. $CHCl_3$, trichloromethane, is also known as chloroform. It is used as a solvent and in the 19th century was used as an anaesthetic. More recently, haloalkanes containing chlorine and fluorine, known as freons or CFCs (structures **14.4**[W] and **14.5**[W]), have been used in refrigerators and aerosols and as blowing agents for the production of foam plastics. However, their use is being phased out because there is very strong evidence that their presence in the atmosphere leads to a depletion of the ozone in the stratosphere.

14.4 **14.5**

14.1.2 Alcohols

Some examples of alcohols are shown in Figure 14.1; they all contain the —OH functional group.

methanol^W CH_3— OH
known as wood spirit, obtained by destructive distillation of wood; used in industry as a solvent; part of the mixture called methylated spirits

ethanol^W CH_3— CH_2 — OH
the alcohol in alcoholic drinks; also part of methylated spirits

heptan-2-ol^W OH | CH_3—CH — CH_2 — CH_2 — CH_2 — CH_2 — CH_3
found in oil of cloves

ethylene glycol (ethane-1,2-diol)^W HO — CH_2 — CH_2 —OH
used in antifreeze

geraniol^W

main constituent of oil of rose and other essential oils

The alcohol functional group can be written as —OH or as HO—

Figure 14.1 Some commonly encountered alcohols.

What are the molecular formula, Lewis structure and structural formula of the simplest alcohol, methanol, which contains only one carbon atom?

CH_4O

molecular formula   Lewis structure   structural formula

In the abbreviated structural formula the alcohol functional group is written as —OH, for example CH_3—OH.

14.1.3 Carboxylic acids

Some typical examples of carboxylic acids are shown in Figure 14.2; they all contain the carboxylic acid functional group

The structural formula of acetic acid (ethanoic acid) is given in Figure 14.2. Draw out the Lewis structure of this acid.

The Lewis structure is shown in the margin.

Notice that one oxygen is bonded to the carbon via a single bond whereas the other is bonded to the carbon by a double bond. For shorthand, this group is often written as —COOH, and we shall adopt this practice where appropriate.

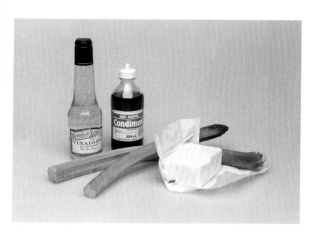

Figure 14.2 Some typical carboxylic acids.

acetic acid^W (ethanoic acid) $CH_3-C\overset{\displaystyle O}{\underset{\displaystyle OH}{\Big<}}$
main constituent of vinegar

butanoic acid^W $CH_3-CH_2-CH_2-C\overset{\displaystyle O}{\underset{\displaystyle OH}{\Big<}}$
gives rise to the smell of rancid butter

hexanoic acid^W $CH_3-CH_2-CH_2-CH_2-CH_2-C\overset{\displaystyle O}{\underset{\displaystyle OH}{\Big<}}$
characteristic smell of goats (not in the picture!)

oxalic acid^W $\underset{\displaystyle HO}{\overset{\displaystyle O}{\Big\|}}C-C\overset{\displaystyle O}{\underset{\displaystyle OH}{\Big\|}}$
found in rhubarb leaves; it is poisonous to humans

The carboxylic acid group can be written as $-C\overset{\displaystyle O}{\underset{\displaystyle OH}{\Big<}}$ or $\overset{\displaystyle O}{\underset{\displaystyle HO}{\Big>}}C-$

14.1.4 Esters

Esters are widespread in nature. They are often pleasant smelling liquids that contribute to the fragrance and flavour of many plants and drinks. Some typical examples are shown in Figure 14.3; they all contain the functional group $-C\overset{\displaystyle O}{\underset{\displaystyle O-}{\Big<}}$

Notice that the difference between esters and carboxylic acids is that in an ester one of the oxygen atoms links two carbon atoms, C—O—C, whereas in a carboxylic acid it is attached to a hydrogen, C—O—H.

Figure 14.3 Some typical esters. Note that, conventionally, benzene rings are drawn without the element symbols C and H, as in the structural formula for methyl salicylate.

ethyl acetate^W (ethyl ethanoate) $CH_3-C\overset{\displaystyle O}{\underset{\displaystyle O-CH_2-CH_3}{\Big<}}$
used as a solvent and a nail varnish remover; smells cf pear drops

methyl butanoate^W $CH_3-CH_2-CH_2-C\overset{\displaystyle O}{\underset{\displaystyle O-CH_3}{\Big<}}$
found in pineapples

isopentyl acetate^W $CH_3-C\overset{\displaystyle O}{\underset{\displaystyle O-CH_2-CH_2-CH-CH_3}{\Big<}}$
$\underset{\displaystyle CH_3}{|}$
constituent of banana oil; used as a flavouring

methyl salicylate^W
oil of wintergreen

The ester group can be written as $-C\overset{\displaystyle O}{\underset{\displaystyle O-}{\Big<}}$ or $\overset{\displaystyle O}{\underset{\displaystyle -O}{\Big>}}C-$

113

So far, when we have introduced a functional group we have usually written the structural formulae in a particular order. For example, we have represented ethanol as CH_3-CH_2-OH. As you saw in the CD-ROM activity 'Introducing functional groups', molecules can be viewed from any angle so it could just as correctly be written as $HO-CH_2-CH_3$. Similarly, acetic acid could be written as:

$$CH_3-\overset{\overset{\textstyle O}{\|}}{C}\underset{OH}{\diagdown} \quad \text{or} \quad \underset{HO}{\overset{\overset{\textstyle O}{\|}}{\diagup}}C-CH_3$$

For the rest of this block we shall write such structures either way round, according to which makes it easier to see what happens in a reaction. Make sure you can recognize the various ways of representing the functional groups: the main representations are shown in the Appendix in the Study File. If you are still not happy, examine the relevant structure on the CD-ROM, using the Weblab molecular viewer, and rotate the structure until you can see how the various representations relate to each other.

Activity 14.2 Analysing the structure of organic compounds

This activity helps you to develop a strategy for analysing the structure of organic compounds. ◀

Activity 14.3 Drawing structural formulae

This activity gives you more practice in drawing structural formulae. ◀

14.2 Characteristic reactions of functional groups

Now you have met some functional groups, let's move on to examine some of the reactions that they undergo. We shall look at some other functional groups later in the block. Remember, the reactions that an organic compound undergoes will depend mainly on the functional group(s) present. The hydrocarbon parts usually act as spectators — in other words they remain unchanged.

14.2.1 Condensation reactions

Figure 14.1 shows that methanol and ethanol contain the alcohol functional group, as does 2-methylbutanol. Although they look different, they undergo the same pattern of reactions. In other words, chemical compounds that react with methanol also react with ethanol and 2-methylbutanol, and chemicals that don't react with methanol, don't react with ethanol or 2-methylbutanol. It is the alcohol functional group, $-OH$, not the saturated hydrocarbon part of the molecule, that controls the reactivity.

One of the reactions that methanol undergoes is with acetic acid to give an ester:

$$CH_3-\overset{\overset{\textstyle O}{\|}}{C}\underset{\boxed{OH \ + \ H}}{\diagdown}\,O-CH_3 \quad \longrightarrow \quad CH_3-\overset{\overset{\textstyle O}{\|}}{C}\underset{O-CH_3}{\diagdown} \ + \ H_2O \qquad (14.1)$$

acetic acid   methanol   an ester

We have used colour to show where the atoms in the acetic acid and the methanol end up in the ester. The box shows which hydrogens and oxygen form water. We have written methanol as $H-O-CH_3$ rather than the more familiar CH_3-OH, to make it easier for you to see which parts end up where in the ester. As this is the reaction of an $-OH$ group, ethanol undergoes the same reaction (Equation 14.2), as does 2-methylbutanol (Equation 14.3).

$$CH_3-\overset{\overset{O}{\|}}{C}\underset{OH}{} + H-O-CH_2-CH_3 \longrightarrow CH_3-\overset{\overset{O}{\|}}{C}\underset{O-CH_2-CH_3}{} + H_2O \qquad (14.2)$$

$$CH_3-\overset{\overset{O}{\|}}{C}\underset{OH}{} + H-O-CH_2-\overset{\overset{CH_3}{|}}{CH}-CH_2-CH_3 \longrightarrow$$

$$CH_3-\overset{\overset{O}{\|}}{C}\underset{O-CH_2-\overset{\overset{CH_3}{|}}{CH}-CH_2-CH_3}{} + H_2O \qquad (14.3)$$

In each case the product is an ester because each compound contains the $-\overset{\overset{O}{\|}}{C}\underset{O-}{}$ group.

As you saw in Activity 14.1, this reaction is one of a group known as **condensation reactions**. Such reactions involve the joining together of two or more molecules to form a larger molecule, together with a small molecule such as water, H_2O, hydrogen chloride, HCl, or ammonia, NH_3. In this case, if an alcohol and acetic acid are heated together in the presence of a catalyst, an ester and *water* are formed. For this reaction the catalyst is a strong acid. We can describe the reaction of acetic acid with any alcohol by using the symbol R to represent the saturated hydrocarbon part of the alcohol molecule:

$$CH_3-\overset{\overset{O}{\|}}{C}\underset{OH}{} + H-O-R \longrightarrow CH_3-\overset{\overset{O}{\|}}{C}\underset{O-R}{} + H_2O \qquad (14.4)$$

Thus Equation 14.4 is the same as Equation 14.1, where $R-OH$ is CH_3-OH, that is R is a CH_3- group.

- Identify the R group in Equations 14.2 and 14.3.

- By analogy with Equation 14.4, in Equation 14.2 R is CH_3-CH_2-, and in

    Equation 14.3 R is $CH_3-CH_2-\overset{\overset{CH_3}{|}}{CH}-CH_2-$

Equation 14.4 showed the reaction between any alcohol and acetic acid. In fact any carboxylic acid could be used here in place of acetic acid. For example, benzoic acid (**14.6**) is a carboxylic acid used as a preservative in foods. Conventionally, the ring in this acid is drawn without the element symbols (**14.7**)[W]. Methanol reacts with benzoic acid to form the ester methyl benzoate:

$$\text{(benzene ring)}-\overset{\overset{O}{\|}}{C}\underset{OH}{} + HO-CH_3 \longrightarrow \text{(benzene ring)}-\overset{\overset{O}{\|}}{C}\underset{O-CH_3}{} + H_2O \qquad (14.5)$$

14.6

14.7

We can develop Equation 14.4 into the more general form:

$$R^1-\overset{\displaystyle O}{\underset{\displaystyle OH}{C}} \quad + \quad HO-R^2 \quad \longrightarrow \quad R^1-\overset{\displaystyle O}{\underset{\displaystyle O-R^2}{C}} \quad + \quad H_2O \tag{14.6}$$

Here we use the symbol R^1 to represent the hydrocarbon group in the carboxylic acid and R^2 to represent the hydrocarbon group in the alcohol. Condensation is another of the key reactions given in the Appendix in the Study File. We shall meet such reactions again.

● Notice that a superscript is used to distinguish one R group from another. Why would a subscript R_2 not be appropriate?

○ Subscripts are used in formulae to tell us how many of the relevant atoms or groups of atoms are present in the molecule. R_2 implies there are two R groups.

The strength of the functional group approach is that, once we have identified a functional group in a compound, all we have to do is to list the reactions and properties of that functional group to be able to predict how the compound will react.

● What key property do you think carboxylic *acids* demonstrate?

○ The name implies they are acids and, as we saw in Section 10, acids dissociate in water to give hydrogen ions.

This dissociation is:

$$CH_3-\overset{\displaystyle O}{\underset{\displaystyle O-H}{C}} \quad \rightleftharpoons \quad CH_3-\overset{\displaystyle O}{\underset{\displaystyle O^-}{C}} \quad + \quad H^+ \tag{14.7}$$

Notice that since the hydrocarbon part of acetic acid is regarded as inert, the hydrogen ion can't come from the methyl group, CH_3-, so it must come from the functional group, $-COOH$, where there is only one hydrogen present. Notice also that after dissociation, there must be a negative charge on the oxygen to balance the positive charge on the hydrogen ion. The negatively charged product is known as a carboxylate ion. Equation 14.7 is the full form of the simplified equation given in Section 7 for the dissociation of acetic acid:

$$HAc \rightleftharpoons H^+ + Ac^- \tag{7.9}$$

● Write out the generalized form of the dissociation in Equation 14.7 using the acid $R-COOH$.

○ $$R-\overset{\displaystyle O}{\underset{\displaystyle OH}{C}} \quad \rightleftharpoons \quad R-\overset{\displaystyle O}{\underset{\displaystyle O^-}{C}} \quad + \quad H^+$$

● Write out the equation for the reaction of a carboxylic acid $R-COOH$ with sodium hydroxide.

○ Sodium hydroxide is an alkali that reacts with acids to give a salt and water. Thus a carboxylic acid reacts with sodium hydroxide to give water and a carboxylate salt:

$$R-\overset{\displaystyle O}{\underset{\displaystyle OH}{C}} \quad + \quad NaOH \quad \longrightarrow \quad R-\overset{\displaystyle O}{\underset{\displaystyle O^-}{C}} \quad + \quad Na^+ \quad + \quad H_2O \tag{14.8}$$

For example, when R is CH_3, the salt is sodium acetate.

14.2.2 Oxidation and reduction

Oxidation and reduction are two key reactions in chemistry. One type of oxidation reaction involves a reaction with oxygen. For example, the all too familiar formation of rust is a reaction of iron with oxygen to give iron oxide:

$$4Fe + 3O_2 \longrightarrow 2Fe_2O_3 \tag{14.9}$$

Because oxygen is added to the iron we say the iron has been oxidized. You may have met another example of an oxidation reaction if you have ever left a bottle of wine open to the air for too long — the alcohol (ethanol) is converted into vinegar (acetic acid), as shown in Equation 14.10. It is an oxidation because the proportion of oxygen in the compound is increased.

$$CH_3-CH_2-OH + O_2 \longrightarrow CH_3-COOH + H_2O \tag{14.10}$$

This oxidation can also be brought about in the laboratory using an aqueous solution of potassium dichromate, $K_2Cr_2O_7$, in the presence of a strong acid, HCl, as shown in Equation 14.11:

$$CH_3-CH_2-OH + K_2Cr_2O_7 \longrightarrow CH_3-COOH \tag{14.11}$$

This equation is not balanced, because we are only interested in the transformation of the organic reactant into the product. The inorganic compound that brings about the oxidation is known as the *reagent* and we are not interested in its fate. Another way of writing this is:

$$CH_3-CH_2-\boxed{OH} \xrightarrow[\text{HCl}]{K_2Cr_2O_7} CH_3-\boxed{COOH}$$

Here the reagents ($K_2Cr_2O_7$ and HCl) are written along the arrow. A generalized reaction scheme for the oxidation is shown in Equation 14.12, using R to represent a hydrocarbon group. Note that in this case, we have written the general formula for the alcohol as $R-CH_2-OH$ *not* $R-OH$; this is because the carbon atom attached to the oxygen is intimately involved in the reaction. (Don't worry too much about this — it's the only time we need to do it in this block.)

$$R-CH_2-\boxed{OH} \xrightarrow[\text{HCl}]{K_2Cr_2O_7} R-\boxed{COOH} \tag{14.12}$$

● Predict the product of the following oxidation:

$$CH_3-CH_2-CH_2-CH_2-\boxed{OH} \xrightarrow[\text{HCl}]{K_2Cr_2O_7} \ ?$$

○ By analogy with Equation 14.12, R is $CH_3-CH_2-CH_2-$, hence the reaction is:

$$CH_3-CH_2-CH_2-CH_2-\boxed{OH} \xrightarrow[\text{HCl}]{K_2Cr_2O_7} CH_3-CH_2-CH_2-\boxed{COOH}$$

● What has happened to the proportion of hydrogen atoms in the molecule during this reaction?

○ The proportion of hydrogen atoms in the molecule has decreased, from ten per molecule to eight per molecule.

This is another way of identifying an oxidation reaction — the loss of hydrogen from a compound.

Reduction is the converse of oxidation. For example, carboxylic acids can be reduced to give alcohols, using hydrogen and a catalyst:

$$CH_3-COOH \xrightarrow{H_2/catalyst} CH_3-CH_2-OH \qquad (14.13)$$

In this reduction the proportion of hydrogen atoms in the molecule is increased and the proportion of oxygen atoms is decreased. Like oxidation, reduction is not limited to organic chemistry; for example, iron oxide (rust) can be converted into elemental iron, by reaction with hydrogen:

$$Fe_2O_3 + 3H_2 \longrightarrow 2Fe + 3H_2O$$

● Is the *hydrogen* oxidized or reduced during this reaction?

○ Because the hydrogen has combined with oxygen to form water, just as the iron did in Equation 14.9, the hydrogen is oxidized.

This illustrates a very important point: any oxidation process is always accompanied by a reduction process and vice versa. If one reactant gains oxygen, the other must lose oxygen, and if one reactant loses hydrogen the other must gain hydrogen. The various ways of describing **oxidation** and **reduction** are summarized in Table 14.2.

Table 14.2 The various ways of defining oxidation and reduction.

Oxidation	Reduction
the proportion of oxygen in the compound increases	the proportion of oxygen in the compound decreases
the proportion of hydrogen in the compound decreases	the proportion of hydrogen in the compound increases

Activity 14.4 Naming of organic compounds

As you meet new functional groups in this section you will come across many compounds with complex sounding names. As we said earlier, you are not expected to learn these names or understand their origin. However, if you are interested in the systematic naming of organic compounds, this activity explains how the system works. ◀

Activity 14.5 Predicting the products of an organic reaction

In this activity you will develop a strategy for predicting the products of an organic reaction. ◀

Question 14.1 Equation 14.13 showed the reduction of acetic acid to ethanol. Write out a generalized scheme for the reduction of any carboxylic acid R—COOH to an alcohol. Predict the organic product of the reduction of benzoic acid (**14.7**). ◀

14.3 Crude oil: final thoughts

As we discussed in Section 12.2, crude oil can be thought of as a mixture of a large number of alkanes, which can be converted into a small number of alkenes. These reactive compounds can be readily transformed into a wide range of substances that can in turn be used to make all the useful things described in Box 13.1. These transformations typify the building block approach, because they start with small molecules that can be interconverted and joined together using predictable, controllable reactions at functional groups.

Rather than giving many more examples of how crude oil eventually ends up in a paint or as a pesticide, it is more useful to look in detail at some representative end uses — plastics and drugs. These will demonstrate how chemistry is employed to design properties into a molecule.

14.4 Summary of Section 14

1   Organic molecules can be classified using the functional group approach. This approach involves the imaginary division of the molecule into parts, the reactive functional group(s) and the unreactive saturated hydrocarbon fragment(s). Only the functional group undergoes reactions, and knowledge of these reactions can be used to predict the properties of an organic compound.

2   The functional groups used most frequently in this block and the key reactions are listed in Appendix 1 in the Study File.

3   A compound is oxidized if the proportion of oxygen in it is increased or the proportion of hydrogen in it is decreased.

4   A compound is reduced if the proportion of oxygen in it is decreased or the proportion of hydrogen in it is increased.

Question 14.2   Identify the functional groups in the following compounds:

(a) $HO-CH_2-CH_2-CH_2-CH_2-CH_2-COOH$

(b)

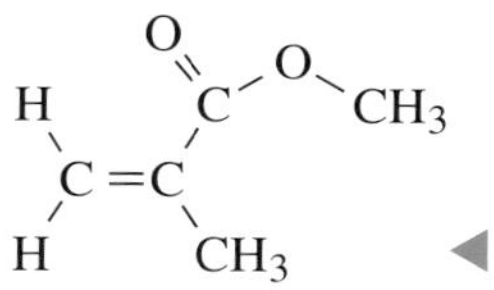

Question 14.3   Draw the Lewis structure of ethanol. How many pairs of non-bonded electrons are there on an oxygen atom in an alcohol? ◀

Question 14.4   Predict the products of the following reactions:

(a) $CH_3-CH_2-CH_2-OH \xrightarrow[HCl]{K_2Cr_2O_7} ?$

(b) $CH_3-CH_2-COOH + CH_3-CH_2-CH_2-CH_2-OH \longrightarrow ?$

(c) $CH_3-CH=CH-CH_3 \xrightarrow{H_2O} ?$ ◀

Question 14.5   Predict the products of the following reactions of leaf alcohol, which occurs in the leaves of some scented plants.

(a) $CH_3-CH_2-CH=CH-CH_2-CH_2-OH + CH_3-COOH \longrightarrow ?$

(b) $CH_3-CH_2-CH=CH-CH_2-CH_2-OH + Br_2 \longrightarrow ?$ ◀

Question 14.6   In the following reactions, is the reactant oxidized or reduced?

(a)

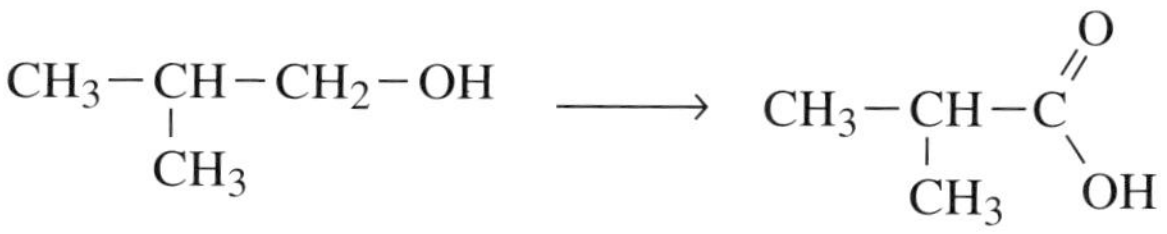

(b) $CH_3-CH=CH_2 \longrightarrow CH_3-CH_2-CH_3$ ◀

15 Polymers

The first group of products derived from crude oil that we shall examine in detail are plastics.

Activity 15.1 Plastics in the home

This activity requires you to relate the properties of some of the plastics in your home to their functions. ◀

The word 'plastics' is a rather colloquial term. A better term, which includes all the materials called plastics, is **polymers**. As we shall see in a moment, a polymer is made up of molecules comprising very long chains of atoms.

To say that polymers are important in our modern world is a gross understatement. Our life depends, and indeed always has depended, on polymers of one sort or another. Our bodies contain many polymers, such as proteins, polysaccharides, DNA and RNA, which you will meet in Block 9. Many of the natural materials that we use are polymers: for example, wood, rubber, cotton, wool, linen and silk. These materials were used for many centuries without any knowledge of their molecular structures. However, as our understanding of their structures has developed we have been able to construct our own polymers. The production of synthetic polymers has revolutionized our society. Much of our clothing is made from polymers such as Nylon, Terylene, Courtelle, Acrilan, Rayon, Viscose and Lycra. When you looked around in Activity 15.1 and saw how many articles are made from synthetic polymers, then you probably realized how dependent we are on their large-scale production. The range of this production is illustrated in Figure 15.1.

Figure 15.1 The world-wide production of different polymers in 1990, as percentages of the total, which was about 100 million tonnes. You will see later in this section how the names of the

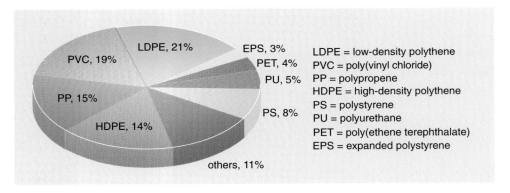

The uses to which polymers are put are legion, from non-stick cooking pans to blood plasma substitutes. The variety of articles depends very much on the ability of the polymer chemist to build in features at the molecular level, and thus to produce the right polymer for the job. Today, it is possible to produce a very hard, rigid polymer to form aeroplane wings, and a soft, pliable polymer for use in rubber gloves. It is possible to produce polymers that are stable at high temperatures, polymers that conduct electricity, polymers that are stronger than steel, and polymers that are strong adhesives. In fact, a polymer can now be manufactured to fit almost any specification. The range and proportions of the uses of polymers in the UK are shown in Figure 15.2.

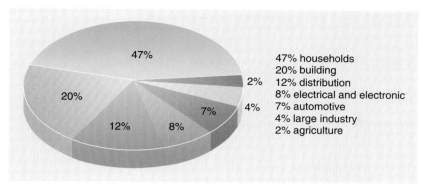

Figure 15.2 The uses of polymers in the UK in 1990, expressed as percentages of the total, which was around 3 million tonnes.

47% households
20% building
12% distribution
8% electrical and electronic
7% automotive
4% large industry
2% agriculture

It was the Roman poet Lucretius who, two thousand years ago, first named historical epochs in terms of the prevalent material of the period, the 'Iron Age', 'Stone Age', etc. If our age were to be named after the dominant materials, it might justifiably be called the 'Polymer Age'.

15.1 What is a polymer?

A polymer is made up of molecules comprising very long chains of atoms. For example, polythene is a saturated hydrocarbon and its molecules are linear chains of many carbon atoms, with hydrogen atoms attached; often there are thousands of carbon atoms joined like a string of pearls. One way of representing such large structures is by the formula $CH_3—(CH_2)_n—CH_3$, where n stands for a very large number, about 1 000–2 000. However, as we shall see later, polymer molecules are not always chains of carbon atoms only; oxygen and nitrogen atoms can also be part of the chain.

Even though the polymer molecule is a chain of atoms, it does not usually exist in a linear form. As you saw in Activity 14.1, rotation about single bonds is easy, so the molecule readily coils up, as shown in Figure 15.3. Now imagine what the polymer must be like with millions and millions of these molecules all physically entangled to produce something like a mass of cooked spaghetti. Clearly, a solid polymer is not like the solids formed by smaller molecules. Small molecules, such as iodine, I_2 (Section 4.2), can form crystals in which the molecules pack together in regular three-dimensional arrangements. On heating, such crystals melt at a particular temperature. Because polymers consist of very large intertwined molecules, they do not form regular crystals. At low temperatures the chains move very little and so the material is hard and brittle. As the temperature is increased, the chains start to move over each other and the polymer softens. This happens over a range of temperatures; a polymer has no precise melting temperature. This softening is important in industry. Polymers such as polythene can be moulded and shaped at a higher temperatures, and they retain this shape when cooled to room temperature. Polymers that are hard at room temperature, but which become soft on heating such that they can be remoulded, are known as **thermoplastic polymers**.

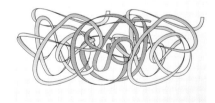

Figure 15.3 The long molecules of a polymer coil up. The coils are not separate from one another but intertwined. For clarity, the chains are drawn as ribbons of different colours.

15.2 Properties of polymers

In Activity 15.1 you saw that polymers can have a range of different properties that determine their uses. Some are brittle, some are tough and some are elastic. This section describes how it is possible to manipulate the molecular structure to obtain such a range of properties.

15.2.1 Hard or elastic?

Natural rubber is an unsaturated hydrocarbon. Its molecules are long chains of carbon atoms with hydrogen atoms attached. It is obtained from the sap of the rubber tree as a latex, a suspension of rubber particles in water. When the rubber has been dried it is elastic, but is sticky and has little strength. In the unstretched form the tangled coils of rubber molecules are held together by London interactions to give a structure like that shown in Figure 15.4a. As the material is stretched the molecules start to disentangle and straighten out in the direction of the extension, as shown in Figure 15.4b. If the force is applied for only a short time, the molecules spring back to their original coiled forms on removal of the force. The material reverts to its original shape; it is elastic. However, if the rubber is stretched for too long or too far, the chains unravel and start to slip over each other, as shown in Figure 15.4c. The material then assumes a new shape.

Figure 15.4 The changes that occur at the molecular level when natural unstretched rubber (a) is stretched by a small amount (b) and by a large amount (c).

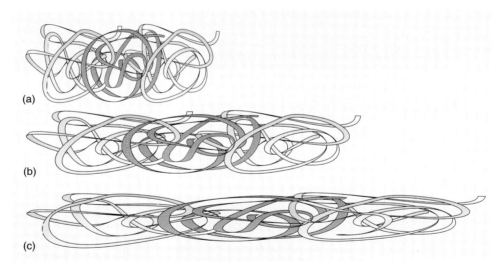

The elastic properties of natural rubber can be improved by a chemical process known as **vulcanization**. This was discovered by Charles Goodyear in the USA in 1839. The discovery was fortuitous, like many in science. Goodyear had been experimenting for many years trying to make rubber more useful. One day he accidentally left a mixture of rubber, sulfur and lead oxide on the stove. When he returned he noticed the rubber was no longer sticky but a tough elastic material. Figure 15.5a shows that vulcanization, the reaction of elemental sulfur with the C=C double bonds in rubber, involves linking together two carbon chains by covalently bonded 'bridges' of sulfur atoms. This gives a huge three-dimensional network of *cross-linked* chains. On stretching, the molecules can still uncoil so the material is elastic, but, as shown in Figure 15.5b, the chains cannot be completely pulled apart from each other, which accounts for its strength. When the rubber is released the molecules coil up again and the material returns to its original shape.

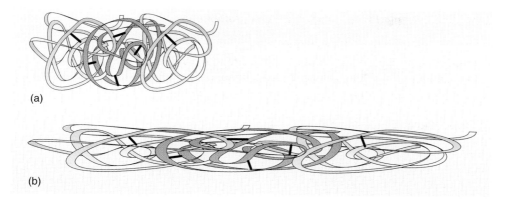

(a)

(b)

Figure 15.5 Cross-linking in vulcanized rubber, (a) unstretched and (b) stretched. The black lines represent the sulfur cross-links.

Vulcanized polymers are elastic irrespective of the time for which the stretching is applied. The use of three parts of sulfur to 100 parts of rubber enables the rubber to be stretched up to eight times its original length and then to return to its original length when the stretching force is removed. Increasing the sulfur content makes the rubber still harder, because so many cross-links are formed that even uncoiling the molecules becomes difficult. Eventually, when sufficient sulfur is added to the rubber, it becomes rigid. This is the material known as ebonite, which can be used for making a variety of things, including woodwind instruments.

Many very hard polymers, such as bakelite and epoxy resins, also consist of chains of atoms that are extensively cross-linked by covalent bonds to give a rigid three-dimensional network. These hard non-elastic materials are known as **thermosetting polymers**. This is because, unlike thermoplastic polymers, they do not soften on heating so they cannot be remoulded once they have been made. In order to remould thermosetting polymers it would be necessary to break the network of covalent cross-links between the chains and this is very difficult. An example of a typical thermosetting polymer is the epoxy resin used in glues such as Araldite. The adhesive requires two materials to be mixed prior to application. One tube contains a treacle-like polymer, whose molecules are linear chains that are not yet cross-linked. The other tube, sometimes called the hardener, contains the cross-linking agent. When the contents of the tubes are mixed, they react to form a three-dimensional network of cross-linked chains and the result is a rigid solid.

15.2.2 Intermolecular interactions in polymers

Cross-linking polymer chains by covalent bonds is one way in which we can control the properties of polymers. Because these cross-links involve covalent bonds they are difficult to break. One set of interactions that are weaker and can therefore be readily broken down and remade are the intermolecular interactions that you met in Section 7, London interactions and hydrogen bonds.

The arrangement of polymer chains is not quite as random as we have described. Polymers often contain small regions where segments of chains line up parallel with one another, as shown in Figure 15.6, held together by intermolecular interactions. These regions are similar to the arrangement of molecules in crystals and so are known as **crystallites**. They increase the opportunity for intermolecular interactions to bind the chains together. Increasing the amount of crystallinity in a polymer increases the extent to which the chains are anchored to each other and thus increases the density, the softening temperature, stiffness, solvent resistance, hardness and load-bearing characteristics of the polymer.

Figure 15.6 A schematic representation of the formation of crystallites by alignment of regions of the polymer chains.

If the polymer chains are held together only by intermolecular interactions, the links can be broken by heating and reformed by cooling. Heating will soften the polymer as the crystallites 'melt' and so the material can be reshaped. As the material cools down new crystallites are formed, and these ensure that the material keeps its new shape. The material is thus thermoplastic.

By controlling the extent of crystallite formation we can determine the properties of a polymer. This in turn involves designing the polymer molecule so that it produces just the right amount of crystallinity. For example, high-density polythene is made up of linear-chain molecules, as shown in Figure 15.7a. In contrast, low-density polythene is made up of chains that have branches of one or more carbon atoms (with their hydrogen atoms), as shown in Figure 15.7b. Usually there are between 7 and 30 branches for every 1 000 carbon atoms in the backbone.

Figure 15.7 The backbone of (a) high-density and (b) low-density polythene.

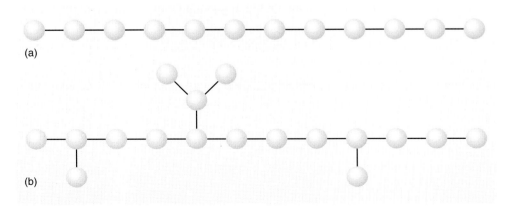

Because of the branches in low-density polythene, the chains cannot get close to each other as easily as they can in the linear-chain form — high-density polythene. Thus, low-density polythene has fewer crystallites than high-density polythene. The chains of low-density polythene are held together to a lesser extent than those of high-density polythene and so it is less rigid and has a lower softening temperature than high-density polythene.

We can make these different polymers match the properties required in the end product. Low-density polythene is less expensive and, because of its flexibility, is used for sheeting, containers and other household goods, such as plastic freezer bags and sandwich bags. High-density polythene is used for, among other things, certain medical equipment, because it can be sterilized with steam without going soft: the low-density form would be deformed because of its lower softening temperature.

15.3 Building links

So far in our discussion of polymers we have not mentioned the detailed structure of the polymer chain or how the chains are made. In fact, a polymer chain is rather like a steel chain. A steel chain is made up of identical links joined together, as shown in Figure 15.8a. The more links in the chain, the longer the chain. Now apply this analogy to the polyester polymer chain shown in Figure 15.8b. The polymer chain is made from identical repeating segments, known as **monomer units** (Greek: *mono*, single; *meros*, part). The length of the chain is determined by the number of units. A polymer molecule (Greek: *poly*, many; *meros*, part) often contains thousands of these monomer units joined together. Now you may appreciate why the polymer shown in Figure 15.8b is called a polyester — it contains many ester groups.

Synthetic polymers have this repeating structure because they are made from very many smaller reactant molecules called **monomers**, which become covalently bonded together in a long chain. Look at the monomer from which the polyester in Figure 15.8b was made, and note the difference between the monomer and the monomer unit. The monomer is the reactant from which the polymer is made. The monomer unit is the repeating segment in the polymer molecule.

Figure 15.8 (a) A steel chain. (b) The chain-like nature of a polyester, and its monomer and monomer unit. When we write a polymer as $-(..........)_n-$ it implies that we are looking at a segment of the polymer made from many, n, monomer units joined together. Because we are looking at a segment of the polymer, the dangling bonds at the ends are where it joins to the rest of the chain.

(a)

(b)

monomer unit

monomer

The process whereby monomers are linked together to give a polymer is called **polymerization**. Whenever a chain is built, be it a steel chain, a daisy chain or a polymer chain, the important property that each link, daisy or monomer, must possess is that it can join to the chain at two places (Figure 15.9).

Figure 15.9   Each unit needs two links to become part of a chain.

For example, if a group of railway carriages have only one coupling each then they can only be joined in pairs. However, if the group have two couplings each, one at each end, they can form a long train. The couplings that monomers have are functional groups, which allow them to form at least two covalent bonds to other monomers, thereby building up long chains. This is another illustration of the central importance of functional groups in organic chemistry.

The type of functional group in the monomer governs the kind of reaction involved in producing the polymer. We shall be concerned with two sorts of reaction, both of which you have met already. These are condensation reactions and addition reactions.

15.3.1 Condensation polymerization

We shall start by considering a reaction between two molecules that each have only one functional group.

Write the equation for the reaction between an alcohol, R^1—OH, and a carboxylic acid, R^2—COOH. What type of reaction is this?

$$R^2 - \overset{\overset{\displaystyle O}{\|}}{C} - OH \;+\; HO - R^1 \longrightarrow R^2 - \overset{\overset{\displaystyle O}{\|}}{C} - O - R^1 \;+\; H_2O$$

This is a condensation reaction because two molecules link up to form a large molecule, an ester in this case, together with a small one, water.

The ester that is formed doesn't undergo any further reaction with the alcohol or the carboxylic acid. Because each reactant contains only one functional group, polymerization isn't possible. A polymer chain is formed only if a molecule can make links to *two other monomers*. One way of achieving this is to have two functional groups within each monomer molecule. For example, monomer **15.1a**[W] (which can be abbreviated to **15.1b**) contains both an alcohol functional group and a carboxylic acid functional group.

$$HO - \overset{\overset{\displaystyle O}{\|}}{C} - CH_2 - CH_2 - CH_2 - CH_2 - CH_2 - CH_2 - OH \qquad HO - \overset{\overset{\displaystyle O}{\|}}{C} - (CH_2)_6 - OH$$

15.1a $\qquad\qquad\qquad\qquad\qquad\qquad\qquad\qquad$ **15.1b**

Two of these molecules can react together to give an ester:

$$HO - \overset{\overset{\displaystyle O}{\|}}{C} - (CH_2)_6 - OH + HO - \overset{\overset{\displaystyle O}{\|}}{C} - (CH_2)_6 - OH \longrightarrow HO - \overset{\overset{\displaystyle O}{\|}}{C} - (CH_2)_6 - O - \overset{\overset{\displaystyle O}{\|}}{C} - (CH_2)_6 - OH + H_2O$$

15.1 $\qquad\qquad\qquad$ **15.1** $\qquad\qquad\qquad\qquad\qquad$ **15.2**

The product **15.2** still has an alcohol group at one end and a carboxylic acid group at the other. These can react with further molecules of the monomer:

$$HO-\overset{\displaystyle O}{\overset{\|}{C}}-(CH_2)_6-O-\overset{\displaystyle O}{\overset{\|}{C}}-(CH_2)_6-OH \quad + \quad HO-\overset{\displaystyle O}{\overset{\|}{C}}-(CH_2)_6-OH$$

15.2   15.1

$$\downarrow$$

$$HO-\overset{\displaystyle O}{\overset{\|}{C}}-(CH_2)_6-O-\overset{\displaystyle O}{\overset{\|}{C}}-(CH_2)_6-O-\overset{\displaystyle O}{\overset{\|}{C}}-(CH_2)_6-OH \quad + \quad H_2O$$

Alternatively, short chains can link together:

$$HO-\overset{\displaystyle O}{\overset{\|}{C}}-(CH_2)_6-O-\overset{\displaystyle O}{\overset{\|}{C}}-(CH_2)_6-OH \quad + \quad HO-\overset{\displaystyle O}{\overset{\|}{C}}-(CH_2)_6-O-\overset{\displaystyle O}{\overset{\|}{C}}-(CH_2)_6-OH$$

$$\downarrow$$

$$HO-\overset{\displaystyle O}{\overset{\|}{C}}-(CH_2)_6-O-\overset{\displaystyle O}{\overset{\|}{C}}-(CH_2)_6-O-\overset{\displaystyle O}{\overset{\|}{C}}-(CH_2)_6-O-\overset{\displaystyle O}{\overset{\|}{C}}-(CH_2)_6-OH \quad + \quad H_2O$$

This process can continue with other monomer molecules so that a long chain is built up; we are well on the way to producing a polymer molecule. The product is known as a **condensation polymer** because it is built up using condensation reactions. In this case, the monomer, the material from which the polymer is made, is **15.1**, and the monomer unit, which is continuously repeated within the chain, is **15.3**.

$$-\overset{\displaystyle O}{\overset{\|}{C}}-(CH_2)_6-O-$$

15.3

There are other ways of drawing the repeating unit for this polymer, for example **15.4**; however, this is *not* the monomer unit. The monomer unit should reflect the way in which the atoms in the monomer end up in the polymer chain, and the dangling bonds should correspond to the bonds that are made when the monomers are joined together. In the condensation reaction that led to this polymer, the bonds that are made are those between the oxygen of the alcohol group and the carbon of the carboxylic acid group, as shown in Equation 14.1. Hence, in the monomer unit, **15.3**, the dangling bonds are from the oxygen of the alcohol group and the carbon of the carboxylic acid group.

$$-O-\overset{\displaystyle O}{\overset{\|}{C}}-(CH_2)_6-$$

15.4

An alternative way of making condensation polymers is to use two different monomers, one that contains *two* alcohol groups and another that contains *two* carboxylic acid groups. Although each monomer contains two functional groups, they cannot readily react with other molecules of the same monomer. However, the two types of monomer can react with each other. For example, compound **15.5** can react with compound **15.6** via a condensation reaction:

$$HO-CH_2-CH_2-OH \quad + \quad HO-\overset{\displaystyle O}{\overset{\|}{C}}-(CH_2)_6-\overset{\displaystyle O}{\overset{\|}{C}}-OH$$

15.5   15.6

$$\downarrow$$

$$HO-CH_2-CH_2-O-\overset{\displaystyle O}{\overset{\|}{C}}-(CH_2)_6-\overset{\displaystyle O}{\overset{\|}{C}}-OH \quad + \quad H_2O$$

The product molecule contains both an alcohol and a carboxylic acid group, so it can react with either type of monomer:

$$HO-CH_2-CH_2-O-\overset{\displaystyle O}{\overset{\|}{C}}-(CH_2)_6-\overset{\displaystyle O}{\overset{\|}{C}}-OH \ + \ HO-CH_2-CH_2-OH$$

$$\downarrow$$

$$HO-CH_2-CH_2-O-\overset{\displaystyle O}{\overset{\|}{C}}-(CH_2)_6-\overset{\displaystyle O}{\overset{\|}{C}}-O-CH_2-CH_2-OH \ + \ H_2O$$

or

$$HO-\overset{\displaystyle O}{\overset{\|}{C}}-(CH_2)_6-\overset{\displaystyle O}{\overset{\|}{C}}-OH \ + \ HO-CH_2-CH_2-O-\overset{\displaystyle O}{\overset{\|}{C}}-(CH_2)_6-\overset{\displaystyle O}{\overset{\|}{C}}-OH$$

$$\downarrow$$

$$HO-\overset{\displaystyle O}{\overset{\|}{C}}-(CH_2)_6-\overset{\displaystyle O}{\overset{\|}{C}}-O-CH_2-CH_2-O-\overset{\displaystyle O}{\overset{\|}{C}}-(CH_2)_6-\overset{\displaystyle O}{\overset{\|}{C}}-OH \ + \ H_2O$$

Again the process can continue to give a long polymer chain. The product is a polyester — each molecule contains many ester groups.

● Perhaps the most famous polyester is Terylene, **15.7**. Which two monomers are used to make Terylene via a condensation reaction?

15.7

○ The colour coding suggests that the polymer is made from **15.8** and **15.9**. In fact **15.8** is the same compound as **15.5**, used to make the previous polyester. Compound **15.9** is like **15.6**, except that it has a benzene ring in the middle instead of a chain of six $-CH_2-$ groups.

15.8   **15.9**

Although polyesters were originally used to make fibres for the manufacture of a variety of textiles, they are now increasingly finding a use in the manufacture of soft-drink bottles. If you look carefully at your local supermarket, you may well see the boxes containing such bottles marked PET, which stands for poly(ethene terephthalate), a polyester.

Amines are another important class of organic compounds that can be used to make condensation polymers, and they are included in the Appendix in the Study File. Amines are akin to ammonia, NH_3, except that they have hydrocarbon groups attached to the nitrogen atom in place of one or more of the hydrogens. They often have unpleasant smells. Two examples are trimethylamine (**15.10**)[W], which smells of rotting fish, and cadaverine (**15.11**)[W], which contains two amine groups and gives rise to the unpleasant smell of decaying flesh.

15.10

$$H_2N-CH_2-CH_2-CH_2-CH_2-NH_2$$

15.11

All amines contain the amine functional group. There are three generalized structures, depending on how many hydrogens are attached to the nitrogen atom:

$$R^2-\underset{\underset{H}{|}}{\overset{\overset{R^1}{|}}{N}}-H \qquad R^2-\underset{\underset{H}{|}}{\overset{\overset{R^1}{|}}{N}}-H \qquad R^2-\underset{\underset{R^3}{}}{\overset{\overset{R^1}{|}}{N}}$$

For example, methylamine, CH_3-NH_2, is an amine, as are dimethylamine, $CH_3-NH-CH_3$, and trimethylamine (**15.10**), in which all three R groups are CH_3.

Amines are basic, that is they react with acids, for example:

$$R-NH_2 + HCl \rightleftharpoons R-NH_3^+ + Cl^- \tag{15.1}$$

The product $RNH_3^+ Cl^-$ is known as an ammonium salt.

Another characteristic reaction of amines that have a hydrogen attached to the nitrogen is their reaction with carboxylic acids to give compounds called amides:

$$CH_3-\underset{\underset{H}{|}}{\overset{\overset{H}{/}}{N}} + HO-\overset{\overset{O}{||}}{C}-CH_3 \longrightarrow CH_3-\underset{\underset{H}{|}}{N}-\overset{\overset{O}{||}}{C}-CH_3 + H_2O$$

$$\underset{CH_3}{\overset{CH_3}{\diagdown}}N-H + HO-\overset{\overset{O}{||}}{C}-CH_3 \longrightarrow \underset{CH_3}{\overset{CH_3}{\diagdown}}N-\overset{\overset{O}{||}}{C}-CH_3 + H_2O$$

The amide group is highlighted, and is also listed in the Study File. Water is also produced in this reaction so it is another example of a condensation reaction. The generalized reaction depends on the number of hydrogens on the nitrogen:

$$R^2-\underset{\underset{H}{\diagdown}}{\overset{\overset{H}{/}}{N}} + HO-\overset{\overset{O}{||}}{C}-R^1 \longrightarrow R^2-NH-\overset{\overset{O}{||}}{C}-R^1 + H_2O \tag{15.2}$$

$$\underset{R^3}{\overset{R^2}{\diagdown}}NH + HO-\overset{\overset{O}{||}}{C}-R^1 \longrightarrow \underset{R^3}{\overset{R^2}{\diagdown}}N-\overset{\overset{O}{||}}{C}-R^1 + H_2O \tag{15.3}$$

Amides are of great biological significance, as you will discover in Block 9. An amide found in the home is 4-hydroxyacetanilide, commonly known as paracetamol (**15.12**)[W].

Amides can have zero, one or two R groups attached to the nitrogen, giving the three generalized structures:

$$R^1-\overset{\overset{O}{||}}{C}\underset{\underset{H}{/}}{\diagdown}N-H \qquad R^1-\overset{\overset{O}{||}}{C}\underset{\underset{R^2}{/}}{\diagdown}N-H \qquad R^1-\overset{\overset{O}{||}}{C}\underset{\underset{R^2}{/}}{\diagdown}N-R^3$$

In paracetamol R^1 is a CH_3- group and R^2 has the structure **15.13**.

15.12

15.13

Question 15.1 Predict the product of each of the following reactions.

(a) $CH_3-NH_2 + CH_3-COOH \longrightarrow$? (condensation reaction)

(b) $CH_3-NH-CH_3 + CH_3-CH_2-COOH \longrightarrow$? (condensation reaction)

(c) $CH_3-CH_2-NH_2 + HCl \longrightarrow$? ◄

Activity 15.2 The formation of nylon

In this activity you will investigate how the condensation of an amine with a carboxylic acid can be used to form the polymer nylon. ◄

15.3.3 Addition polymers

In Section 13.1 you saw that compounds with double bonds, such as ethene, can take part in addition reactions to form two new single bonds to other atoms or groups of atoms, for example:

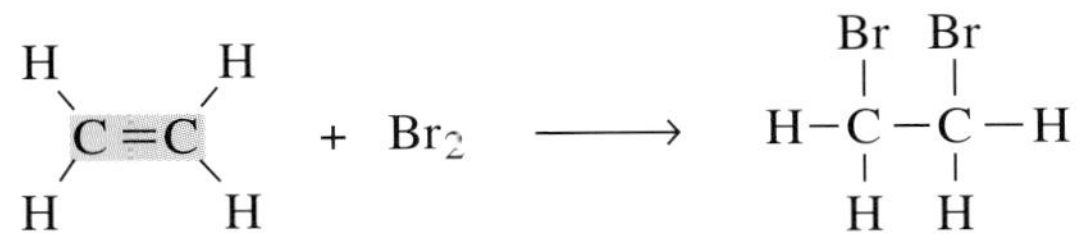

$$\begin{array}{c} H \\ \diagdown \\ \diagup \\ H \end{array} C = C \begin{array}{c} H \\ \diagup \\ \diagdown \\ H \end{array} \ + \ Br_2 \ \longrightarrow \ \begin{array}{c} Br \ \ Br \\ | \ \ \ | \\ H-C-C-H \\ | \ \ \ | \\ H \ \ H \end{array}$$

In 1933, R. O. Gibson and E. W. Fawcett at Imperial Chemical Industries found that when ethene was heated under high pressure a hard waxy solid was formed, which appeared to contain only carbon and hydrogen atoms in the ratio 1 : 2. They concluded that instead of adding to a *different* type of molecule, the ethene molecules had linked *to one another*:

$$CH_2=CH_2 \ + \ CH_2=CH_2 \ + \ CH_2=CH_2 \ + \ CH_2=CH_2$$

$$\downarrow$$

$$-CH_2-CH_2-CH_2-CH_2-CH_2-CH_2-CH_2-CH_2-$$

In this process, one of the bonds in the carbon–carbon double bond of each of the ethene monomers (shown in red above) is broken, and each carbon forms a new bond (also shown in red) to another monomer. This polymer of ethene is *polyethene*, commonly known as polythene. This seems to contradict our earlier criterion for polymer formation. Ethene only contains one functional group, yet it forms a polymer. However, because an addition reaction can form *two* new bonds, it can produce an **addition polymer**. It is a special type of polymerization involving monomers that contain a carbon–carbon double bond; such monomers can form *two* new covalent bonds to other monomers.

A large number of different polymers are produced by addition polymerization using monomers of the type $CH_2=CH-X$, where X can be one of a range of atoms or groups, as shown in Table 15.1.

Table 15.1 Some addition polymers and their monomers.

Monomer name[a]	Abbreviated structural formula of monomer	Polymer name
vinyl chloride (chloroethene)[W]	$CH_2{=}CH{-}Cl$	poly(vinyl chloride) or PVC
propylene (propene)[W]	$CH_2{=}CH{-}CH_3$	polypropylene
styrene (phenylethene)[W]	$CH_2{=}CH{-}\bigcirc$	polystyrene

[a] The common name in the polymer industry is given first, with the systematic name in parentheses.

The general equation for this type of addition polymerization is:

$$CH_2{=}CH{-}X \ + \ CH_2{=}CH{-}X \ + \ CH_2{=}CH{-}X \ + \ CH_2{=}CH{-}X$$

$$\downarrow$$

$$-CH_2-\overset{\overset{\textstyle X}{|}}{CH}-CH_2-\overset{\overset{\textstyle X}{|}}{CH}-CH_2-\overset{\overset{\textstyle X}{|}}{CH}-CH_2-\overset{\overset{\textstyle X}{|}}{CH}-$$

The monomer unit for these polymers is $-CH_2-CHX-$, which reflects the way in which the atoms in the monomer end up in the polymer chain and the bonds that are made in the reaction when the monomers are joined together. By choosing a monomer with a particular group X, we are able to design properties into the polymer. For example, the monomer **15.14** contains a $C{=}C$ double bond that can be polymerized. In the absence of water the resulting polymer is hard and rigid. However, in the presence of water, the $-OH$ groups in the polymer can form hydrogen bonds with the water molecules such that water is absorbed into the body of the material, causing it to swell. The water makes the material soft, and it can thus be used to make contact lenses. The clear flexible gel resembles a film of water covering the eye, reducing irritation.

$$CH_2{=}\overset{\overset{\textstyle CH_3}{\diagup}}{\underset{\underset{\textstyle O}{\diagdown\!\!/}}{C}}\!\!-\!O\!-\!CH_2\!-\!CH_2\!-\!OH$$

15.14

15.4 What has this got to do with crude oil?

The explosion in the use of polymers has depended on a ready supply of monomers.

⬤ Where do monomers such as ethene and propene come from?

◯ These compounds are products of the oil industry. They are obtained by cracking crude oil (Section 13.1).

The monomers in Table 15.1 used to make addition polymers can all be made from the alkenes obtained from crude oil. Figure 15.10 shows how some of these are obtained. The monomers used in condensation polymerization, such as ethane-1,2-diol, can also be obtained from ethenes. In fact all of the monomers that we have mentioned in this section can be built up from smaller molecules that are obtained from crude oil.

Figure 15.10 Various monomers can be made from ethene and propene, etc., which are themselves made from crude oil. Note that parentheses are used in polymer names when there is more than one word after the 'poly' prefix.

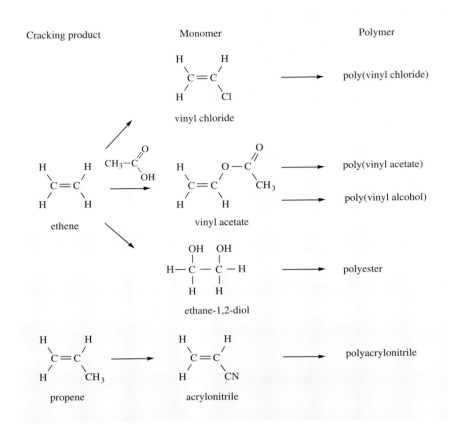

15.5 Summary of Section 15

1   Polymers are long-chain molecules made from smaller molecules, known as monomers, by a process called polymerization. Monomers are able to form at least two bonds to other monomers. When monomers react together to form a polymer, the monomer changes and becomes the monomer unit.

2   Thermosetting polymers cannot be remoulded once formed. They are produced by forming covalent cross-links between the polymer chains to give a three-dimensional network. Vulcanized rubber returns to its original shape when stretched.

3   Thermoplastic polymers can be remoulded once formed. No covalent cross-links are present. The tangle of polymer chains form crystallites, in which the chains line up and are held together by intermolecular interactions. The amount of crystallite formation depends on how well the chains can pack together.

4   Condensation polymers are produced from monomers with two functional groups, where the links between the monomers are formed in condensation reactions.

5   Addition polymers are produced from alkene monomers. One of the bonds in each C=C double bond is broken and two new bonds to other monomers are formed.

Question 15.2   (a) Given the following polymers and the monomers that formed them, identify the monomer unit.

polymer   monomer

(i) $-CH_2-\underset{\underset{Cl}{|}}{CH}-CH_2-\underset{\underset{Cl}{|}}{CH}-CH_2-\underset{\underset{Cl}{|}}{CH}-CH_2-\underset{\underset{Cl}{|}}{CH}-$ $CH_2=\underset{\underset{Cl}{\diagdown}}{\overset{\overset{H}{\diagup}}{C}}$

polymer   monomer

(ii) $-\overset{\overset{O}{||}}{C}-CH_2-CH_2-CH_2-O-\overset{\overset{O}{||}}{C}-CH_2-CH_2-CH_2-O-$ $HO-\overset{\overset{O}{||}}{C}-CH_2-CH_2-CH_2-OH$

(b) Given the following polymer and monomer unit, identify the monomer.

polymer   monomer unit

$\underset{-CH_2-CH-CH_2-CH-CH_2-CH-}{\overset{\overset{O\diagdown}{C}\diagup^{OH}\ \overset{O\diagdown}{C}\diagup^{OH}\ \overset{O\diagdown}{C}\diagup^{OH}}{|\qquad\quad|\qquad\quad|}}$ $\underset{-CH_2-CH-}{\overset{\overset{O\diagdown}{C}\diagup^{OH}}{|}}$ ◀

Question 15.3   Identify the monomer unit and the monomer in the following polymers.

(a) $-CH_2-\underset{\underset{CH_3}{|}}{CH}-CH_2-\underset{\underset{CH_3}{|}}{CH}-CH_2-\underset{\underset{CH_3}{|}}{CH}-CH_2-\underset{\underset{CH_3}{|}}{CH}-$

(b) $-\overset{\overset{O}{||}}{C}-CH_2-CH_2-NH-\overset{\overset{O}{||}}{C}-CH_2-CH_2-NH-\overset{\overset{O}{||}}{C}-CH_2-CH_2-NH-$ ◀

Question 15.4   Would a polymer be formed:

(a) from the condensation of CH_3-COOH (acetic acid) with $H_2N-(CH_2)_6-NH_2$ (hexane-1,6-diamine);

(b) from the condensation of CH_3-NH_2 (methylamine) with hexanedioic acid (**15.15**)?   ◀

$HO-\overset{\overset{O}{||}}{C}-(CH_2)_4-\overset{\overset{O}{||}}{C}-OH$

15.15

Question 15.5   One important monomer is tetrafluoroethene, $CF_2=CF_2$, which gives the polymer known variously as PTFE (polytetrafluoroethene), or Teflon, used to coat non-stick cooking pans. Draw the polymer chain.   ◀

Activity 15.3 Demonstrating the relationship between the structure of poly(vinyl alcohol) and its physical properties

In this activity you can investigate the properties of polymers using readily available materials that you may have around the home.   ◀

16 Pharmaceuticals

Even though proper nutrition and good hygiene go a long way in maintaining a healthy life, our bodies are assailed by a host of agents that can cause illness and disease.

- List some of the agents that may cause illness and disease.

- Your list may contain such things as viruses, fungi and bacteria.

Degeneration of the body may also be caused by genetic diseases and general breakdown of the system of chemical reactions in the body that maintain life. All of these factors can lead to temporary or long-term health problems. One of the ways of preventing and combating such problems is through the use of pharmaceuticals (drugs) — chemicals useful in the therapeutic treatment of disease or in clinical practice.

In this section we shall look at some of the chemistry of drug action and some of the thinking that goes into the design of new drugs. Most drugs in common use are organic compounds, often made via a circuitous route from crude oil. We shall start by looking at aspirin.

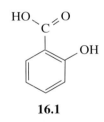

16.1

16.1 How aspirin was discovered

Like many drugs, aspirin was developed from a natural remedy. Hippocrates (Figure 16.1) recommended the use of willow bark for pain control during childbirth. In 30 AD, Aulus Cornelius Celsus suggested the use of a vinegar extract of willow bark as a remedy for rheumatic pain. The active ingredient, called salicin, was first isolated from willow bark in 1829 by Leroux; it was salicylic acid (**16.1**)[W].

Figure 16.1 Hippocrates of Cos (460–370 BC) studied with Democritus, one of the founders of the atomic theory. He spent most of his life travelling around curing the great of obscure diseases and ridding cities of plague. He was one of the first physicians to suggest that disease is a malfunction of the body and arises from factors such as the food eaten, rather than a result of astrological or spiritual factors. His name is immortalized in the Hippocratic oath.

Question 16.1   Use the strategy you developed in Activity 14.2 to analyse the structure of salicylic acid. Identify the framework of carbon atoms and the functional groups and their relative positions. For the purposes of this question assume that the benzene ring is not a functional group, but provides the carbon framework. ◀

● How is salicylic acid likely to react with sodium hydroxide?

○ Sodium hydroxide is an alkali, which reacts with acids to give a salt and water. Salicylic acid contains a carboxylic acid functional group that undergoes a neutralization reaction, as shown in Equation 14.8. Thus salicylic acid reacts with sodium hydroxide to give water and sodium salicylate, which is a carboxylate salt:

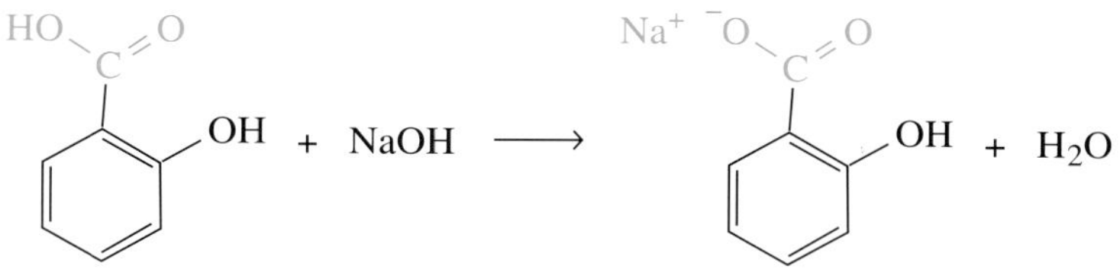

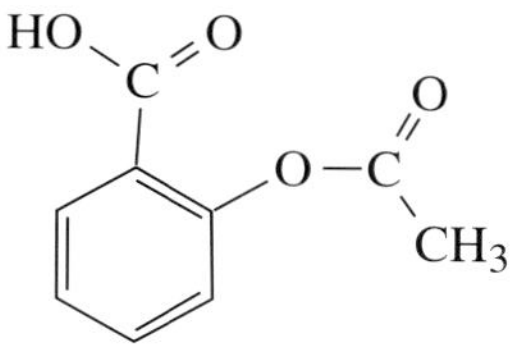

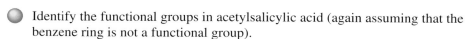

Sodium salicylate was first used for the treatment of rheumatic fever in 1875. However, it had the disadvantage of causing severe irritation of the stomach. The father of an employee of the Bayer Chemical Company pleaded with his son to find a less irritating drug. Many compounds based on salicylic acid were examined, and acetylsalicylic acid (**16.2**)[W] was found to be the best. In 1899, Bayer introduced aspirin, the active component of which is acetylsalicylic acid, as a drug effective against fevers, pain and arthritis. The name aspirin was derived by adding an 'a' for acetyl to spirin, which came from the name of the plant, *Spiraea ulmania*, from which the salicylic acid[*] was prepared.

16.2

● Identify the functional groups in acetylsalicylic acid (again assuming that the benzene ring is not a functional group).

○ Acetylsalicylic acid contains a carboxylic acid functional group and an ester functional group.

● What is the relationship between acetylsalicylic acid and salicylic acid?

○ Acetylsalicylic acid is an ester, which is derived from the alcohol functional group of salicylic acid, not from the carboxylic acid group.

As you might expect, acetylsalicylic acid can be prepared by the condensation reaction of salicylic acid with acetic acid:

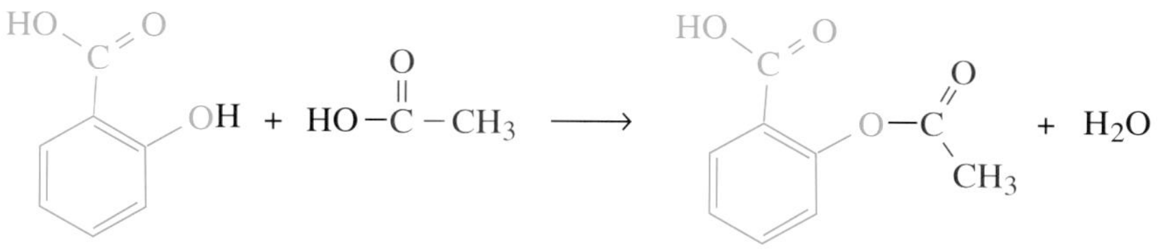

This story of aspirin demonstrates an important way in which drugs are discovered. Traditional herbal medicines often provide a starting point. The active ingredient can be isolated and then the structure determined. By making a series of slight

[*]In this section, because of the complexity of the systematic names we shall use the more traditional names of the compounds.

Figure 16.2 We still talk of taking our prescriptions to the chemist, when we really mean the pharmacist! The confusion has arisen because shops that dispense medicines used to be called 'Chemists and Druggists' because they sold other chemicals for house and garden use. Nowadays you cannot buy such chemicals over the counter, and medicines are obtained from a pharmacist. However, the chemist label hasn't gone away completely.

modifications to the structure of the active compound, a more effective drug may be developed which may have fewer side effects. Some people may be tempted to suggest that the natural compound is 'healthier' than the synthetic compound, but remember that the plant produces salicylic acid for its own purposes, not to cure our headaches. Only through a process of trial and error was it found that it also relieved pain. It is up to the ingenuity of the chemist (see Figure 16.2) to build on what nature has provided and develop safer and more effective alternatives.

16.2 How drugs work

To understand how drugs work we need to examine, briefly, some of the chemistry that goes on inside an organism. A more thorough understanding will be gained in Block 9. As you saw in Block 4, organisms take in chemicals — the food they eat or oxygen from the air — which then undergo various transformations to supply materials for building and repairing the organism and to supply energy. These processes are collectively called metabolism, and they are essentially chemical in nature. However, the system of reactions that perform these tasks in the body is very complex, and each reaction or series of reactions is carried out in a controlled and balanced fashion. Illness is often associated with a change in the rate and balance of some of these reactions. Thus, one way of curing the illness is to influence these reactions so they return to their normal state. This is essentially how many drugs work. Put simply, they are chemicals that can influence the reactions that go on in the body. That is why their choice and dose are so important. First, we need the right chemical to influence the right set of reactions that are out of kilter in the body. Second, we need to give the right dose; too little will have no effect, whereas too much may lead to complete shutdown of a particular set of reactions or to unwanted effects on other sets of reactions.

One of the ways that drugs work is by affecting the properties of compounds known as enzymes. Enzymes are nature's catalysts, and they are very effective at their job. Like all catalysts, they provide an alternative faster reaction pathway to that followed by the uncatalysed reaction. They enable reactions to take place in the body that would require quite stringent and extreme conditions in the laboratory. Enzymes are members of a group of compounds called proteins — natural polymers that are discussed in Box 16.1, *Proteins*.

Box 16.1   Proteins

Proteins are biopolymers — long-chain biological molecules made by joining together smaller monomers. The monomers in this case are called **amino acids** because they contain both an amine (sometimes called amino) functional group and a carboxylic acid functional group. In nature there are about 20 different amino acids with the common structure:

$$H_2N-CH-C \overset{R}{\underset{OH}{\overset{O}{\|}}}$$

Each of the 20 amino acids has a different R group. In the case of amino acids we use R to represent the rest of the molecule, which may include other functional groups, rather than a saturated hydrocarbon chain.

What is the structure of the amino acid in which R is CH_3?

The amino acid (called alanine[W]) has the structure:

$$H_2N-CH-C \overset{CH_3}{\underset{OH}{\overset{O}{\|}}}$$

Just as nylon, a polyamide, could be made by the amine group of one monomer reacting with the carboxylic acid group of another, so the amine group of one amino acid can react with the carboxylic acid group of another amino acid. Condensation polymerization of amino acids leads to proteins, which are also polyamides:

$$-HN-CH-\overset{R^1}{\underset{}{\overset{O}{C}}}-HN-CH-\overset{R^2}{\underset{}{\overset{O}{C}}}-HN-CH-\overset{R^3}{\underset{}{\overset{O}{C}}}-$$

Because there are 20 different amino acids, each with different R groups, there are very many different orders in which these amino acids can be arranged along the polymer chain, giving a vast number of possible proteins.

There are two types of protein: fibrous protein, which occurs in structural material, such as hair and skin, and globular protein, such as enzymes. The order in which the amino acids are linked is fixed for globular protein, such that each long-chain molecule is identical. The sequence of R groups along the chain is the same for all molecules of a particular globular protein. On the other hand, the individual chains of a fibrous protein are not identical. The molecules of a particular fibrous protein are made from similar amino acids, but the order of R groups is not always the same. However, particular sequences of R groups are often repeated within the chains.

Figure 16.3 Two representations of the enzyme trypsin: (a) with the active site empty and (b) with the active site occupied by a protein, shown in green.

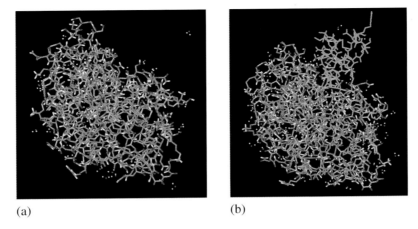

(a)   (b)

Unlike synthetic polymers, which have a relatively random three-dimensional shape, globular proteins coil up in a precise fashion to take up a specific shape. Figure 16.3 shows two representations of the enzyme trypsin[W], which catalyses the breakdown of food protein in the gut. As Figure 16.3a shows, the enzyme is an extremely large protein molecule. It contains about 3 000 atoms, mostly carbon, hydrogen, oxygen and nitrogen, and has a relative molecular mass of 23 800. If you use the molecular viewer software to look at the structure of trypsin, you will get a better idea of its three-dimensional shape. Each molecule of trypsin has this same shape because the sequence of R groups along the chain is the same in every molecule.

We don't need to worry about most of the features of this molecule; we just need to concentrate on an area called the active site, which is shown in Figure 16.3b. It is at this site that the protein in food is converted into smaller molecules. Effectively, a particular segment of the long-chain food protein fits into the active site of the enzyme like a hand into a glove. This site provides the segment of the food protein with the ideal environment for reaction with water, which results in the food protein being broken into two. This reaction is described in Box 16.2, *Hydrolysis*.

Box 16.2   Hydrolysis

One of the key reactions of esters and amides is their reaction with water. This is known as **hydrolysis** and is essentially the reverse of a condensation reaction. For example, an ester reacts with water to give a carboxylic acid and an alcohol; this is usually carried out in the presence of an acid or a base to speed up the reaction:

This part forms the acid

$$R^1-C \overset{O}{\underset{O-R^2}{\big\backslash}} \quad + \quad H_2O \longrightarrow R^1-C \overset{O}{\underset{OH}{\big\backslash}} \quad + \quad HO-R^2 \tag{16.1}$$

This bond is broken

This part forms the alcohol

This reaction is the exact reverse of a condensation so we can write it as an equilibrium:

$$R^1-C \overset{O}{\underset{O-R^2}{\big\backslash}} \quad + \quad H_2O \underset{\text{condensation}}{\overset{\text{hydrolysis}}{\rightleftharpoons}} R^1-C \overset{O}{\underset{OH}{\big\backslash}} \quad + \quad HO-R^2$$

⬤ How can the concentrations of the reactants or products be changed so that (a) hydrolysis predominates or (b) condensation predominates?

◯ If the concentration of one of the reactants or products is increased or decreased it will favour one side of the equilibrium, in accord with Le Chatelier's principle. For example, hydrolysis is favoured by using a high concentration of water. It is for this reason that many hydrolysis reactions are carried out using water as the solvent. Condensation can be favoured using a high concentration of carboxylic acid or alcohol — usually alcohol, which is used as the solvent.

The term hydrolysis comes from the Greek *hydro*, meaning water and *lysis*, meaning split.

⬤ The hydrolysis of amides is the exact reverse of the condensation reaction discussed in Section 15.3.1. Complete the following hydrolysis reaction.

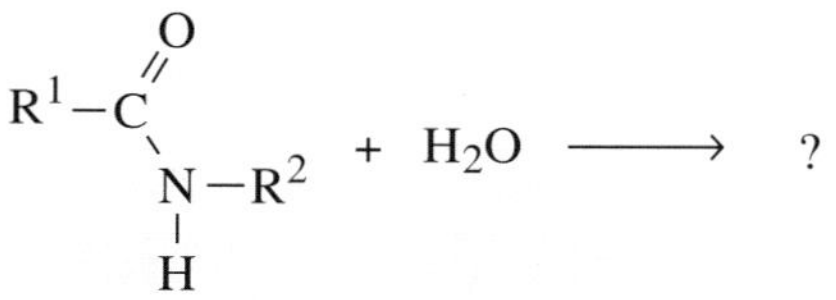

$$R^1-\underset{\underset{\underset{H}{|}}{N-R^2}}{\overset{\overset{O}{\|}}{C}} \ +\ H_2O \ \longrightarrow\ ?$$

◯ Equation 15.2 shows that a carboxylic acid reacts with an amine to give an amide and water:

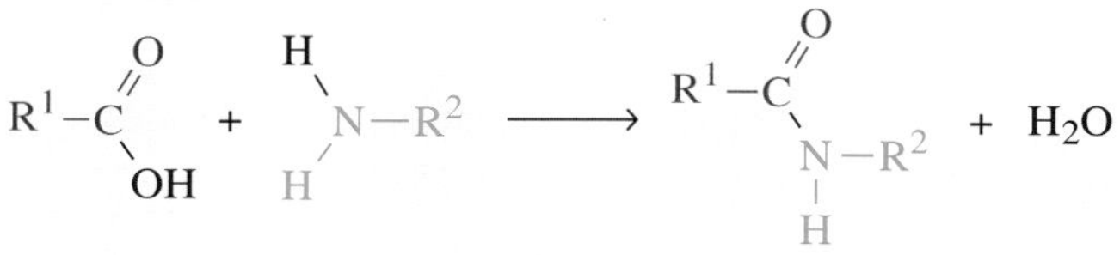

$$R^1-\underset{OH}{\overset{O}{\|}}{C} \ +\ \underset{H}{\overset{H}{\diagdown}}{N-R^2} \ \longrightarrow\ R^1-\underset{\underset{\underset{H}{|}}{N-R^2}}{\overset{\overset{O}{\|}}{C}} \ +\ H_2O \qquad (15.2)$$

As hydrolysis is the reverse of this reaction we can write

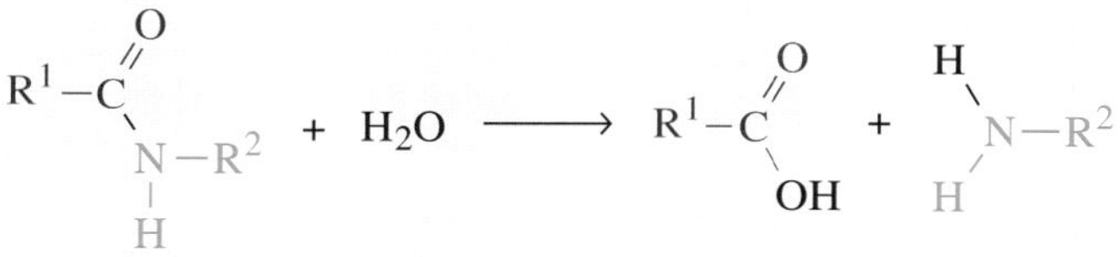

$$R^1-\underset{\underset{\underset{H}{|}}{N-R^2}}{\overset{\overset{O}{\|}}{C}} \ +\ H_2O \ \longrightarrow\ R^1-\underset{OH}{\overset{O}{\|}}{C} \ +\ \underset{H}{\overset{H}{\diagdown}}{N-R^2} \qquad (16.2)$$

Hydrolysis is very important in biological systems. For example, proteins are made by a condensation reaction of amino acids to give a biopolymer in which the monomer units are linked by amide bonds. Hydrolysis provides a way of breaking these amide bonds. Complete hydrolysis of a protein results in conversion into the constituent amino acids.

Question 16.2   What are the products of the following reactions?

(a) 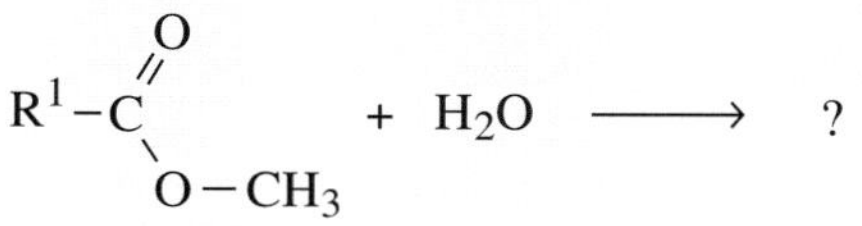 $\quad R^1-\underset{O-CH_3}{\overset{O}{\|}}{C} \ +\ H_2O \ \longrightarrow\ ?$

(b) 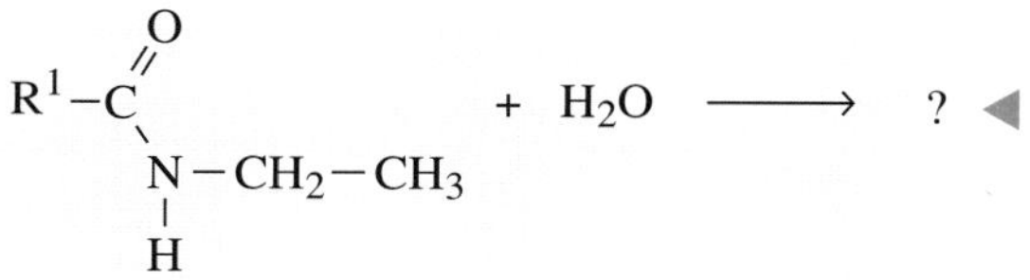 $\quad R^1-\underset{\underset{\underset{H}{|}}{N-CH_2-CH_3}}{\overset{\overset{O}{\|}}{C}} \ +\ H_2O \ \longrightarrow\ ?$ ◀

Because reactant molecules have a three-dimensional shape, and because the active site fits like a glove, the active site must have a specifically shaped three-dimensional hole that will accommodate only a very limited range of reactant molecules (Figure 16.4). As we shall see in a moment, this is the key to drug action. This relationship between enzyme and reactant has also been likened to a lock and key: the key fits the lock and will turn it; the reactant fits the active site and reaction occurs.

Figure 16.4 A schematic representation of the relationship between the active site of an enzyme and reactant molecules: only one of the three reactants shown has exactly the right shape to fit the active site.

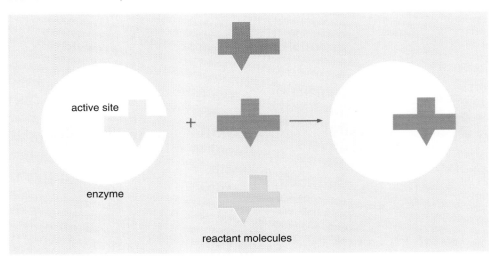

Enzymes provide one way of controlling the metabolic reactions in an organism. Since enzymes are catalysts they are not consumed during a reaction. So once an enzyme molecule has catalysed the conversion of one molecule of reactant into product it is available to catalyse the conversion of more molecules of reactant into product. Thus, only a relatively small amount of an enzyme is needed to catalyse the conversion of a large amount of reactant into product. One of the ways in which an organism 'turns on' a reaction is to supply an active enzyme; the more it provides, the faster the reactant is converted into the product. To slow down or turn off the reaction, the organism simply removes the active enzyme. If we can control the amount of active enzymes in the organism, then we may be able to control the reaction or sets of reactions that are out of kilter. This is one of the ways that drugs work, by affecting the amount of active enzymes. Let's look at an example to make this clearer.

16.2.1 Enzyme action: formation of covalent bonds

Although aspirin has been taken for many years, its mode of action has only recently been discovered. Aspirin is classed as an analgesic (it reduces pain), as an antipyretic (it lowers the temperature of the body if you have a fever), and as an anti-inflammatory drug (it reduces inflammation). It does all this by reducing the concentration, in particular parts of the body, of a group of compounds called prostaglandins. You don't need to know the structures of these compounds, which are quite complex, or about their role in controlling body temperature or causing pain, etc. Suffice it to say that aspirin inhibits the production of prostaglandins in the body.

Prostaglandins are all made in a similar way. One of the first steps in their production involves an enzyme known as cyclo-oxygenase. Aspirin has the right shape to fit into the active site of the cyclo-oxygenase enzyme, where it reacts with an alcohol group attached to one of the amino acids in the protein that makes up the enzyme, as shown in Figure 16.5.

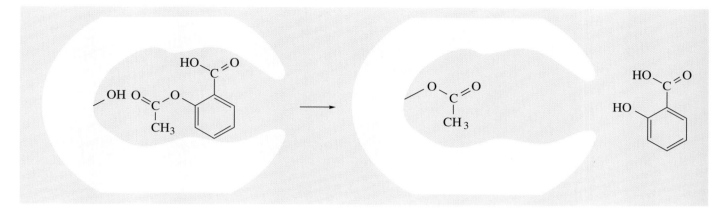

The reaction in Figure 16.5 is not one of the reactions in Appendix 1 in the Study File. Look at the functional groups in the reactant and the product, and describe what changes are taking place.

The carboxylic acid group of the aspirin remains unchanged during the reaction. The alcohol group of the amino acid reacts with the ester of the aspirin to give a new ester, which is attached to the enzyme, and salicylic acid.

Figure 16.5 Aspirin blocks the active site in cyclo-oxygenase by forming a new covalent bond, to give an ester.

Once the new ester group is covalently bound to the cyclo-oxygenase enzyme, it blocks the active site so no other molecules can get in to make prostaglandins. Thus, the enzyme can no longer function as a catalyst. It is rather like blocking a lock with superglue; the key can no longer get in. The reaction of aspirin with the enzyme reduces the concentration of effective catalyst and so the reaction slows down. This means that, overall, prostaglandin production is reduced and the pain goes away. Only when the body makes unblocked enzyme does prostaglandin production start up again.

Besides covalent bond formation, drugs can also block enzymes via intermolecular interactions.

16.2.2 Enzyme action: intermolecular interactions

Figure 16.6 shows the molecular structures of three compounds that act on the central nervous system. Adrenaline is found naturally in the body, and pseudoephedrine is the active ingredient in medicines, such as Actifed and Sudafed, that are used to relieve nasal and respiratory congestion. Salbutamol, or Ventolin, is used in inhalers for asthma relief.

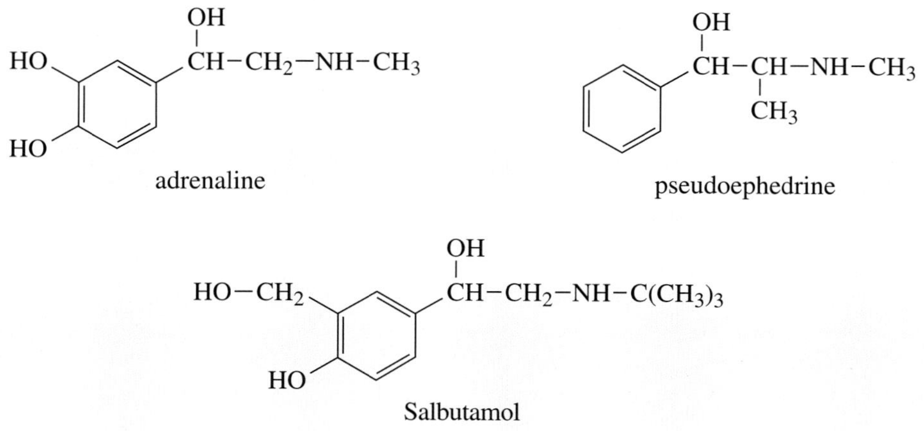

Figure 16.6 The structural formulae of some compounds that act on the central nervous system.

adrenaline

pseudoephedrine

Salbutamol

$$\text{OH}$$

CH−CH−NH−

16.3

○ What features are present in all three molecules?

○ They each contain an alcohol, an amine functional group and a benzene ring, and these three features have the same relative positions in each molecule, as shown in the partial structure **16.3**.

Despite the different uses to which these compounds are put, they all work in the same way. Unlike aspirin they do not act on an enzyme but on a compound called a receptor. One of the ways that chemical reactions are controlled in the body is through the use of specific chemicals that act as 'messengers'. To promote a bodily function, a particular chemical is made at one site in the body and is then transported in the bloodstream to another site, where the chemical messenger interacts with large molecules known as **receptors**, which trigger the required response. Like enzymes, receptors are proteins and, also like enzymes, they have a specific site that will effectively accommodate only one shape and type of molecule. When a messenger molecule binds to a receptor, it stimulates the process it was sent out to initiate, such as the contraction of smooth muscle. All of the compounds in Figure 16.6 act by attaching themselves to receptors. For example, adrenaline is a natural hormone that is released into the bloodstream by the adrenal gland, which is on top of the kidneys, and acts on distant organs such as the heart, lungs, uterus and digestive tract. At each organ, it binds to a receptor but its action varies from site to site. For example, it can widen the bronchial airway and it can increase blood pressure.

Around 10% of the population of developed countries suffer from asthma, and Salbutamol is one of the major drugs that provides relief during a spasm, which is caused by narrowing of the bronchial airways. It does this by mimicking adrenaline and causing the bronchial airway to widen. However, unlike adrenaline, it does not affect other organs, such as the heart. To understand how Salbutamol does this, we need to examine how compounds, such as those in Figure 16.6, bind to receptors.

It is a fairly general rule that drugs are rarely bound to receptors by covalent bonds. Covalent bonds, such as C−C, C−O, or C−N single bonds, are very strong and would require a large amount of energy to break them once formed. Thus, if a drug is bound to a receptor via a covalent bond it would be difficult to remove and the organ would be continuously stimulated, which is not usually the required response. It is better if drugs are held in the receptor by intermolecular interactions of the kinds we discussed in Section 7. These interactions are relatively weak, and easier to break than covalent bonds. This means that the drug binds to the receptor for long enough to have the desired effect. However, because it is held in the receptor by relatively weak interactions, after a while it will leave the receptor and the body will return to its previous state.

○ What intermolecular interactions have you met that might help bind a molecule to a receptor surface?

○ Hydrogen bonds and London interactions.

Hydrogen bonds certainly provide suitable interactions for drug binding. For example, if the surface of a receptor site has a hydrogen with a $\delta+$ charge, it can form a hydrogen bond to an oxygen atom in the drug molecule, for example in an ester group. This is shown schematically in Figure 16.7.

Interactions between ions of opposite charge are also significant in the context of drug binding (although still weak compared with covalent bonds). A suitable pair of functional groups for an ionic interaction are a negatively charged carboxylate ion

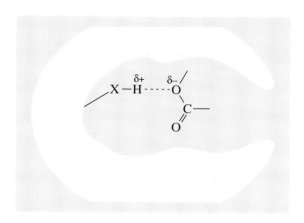

Figure 16.7 Typical hydrogen bonding at a receptor site: X can be a sulfur atom, an oxygen atom or a nitrogen atom.

and a positively charged ammonium ion (Figure 16.8). We have called this an ionic interaction rather than ionic bonding because ionic bonding arises from a network of very many positive and negative charges where ions of opposite charge are small and relatively close to each other, as in Figure 4.4. An ionic interaction involves an attraction between isolated positively and negatively charged groups that are usually farther apart.

carboxylate ion   ammonium ion

Figure 16.8 A negatively charged carboxylate ion and a positively charged ammonium ion will attract one another.

If there is a receptor molecule with a long hydrocarbon chain, and a drug molecule also with a long hydrocarbon chain, it may well happen that the two chains line up side-by-side, as a result of hydrophobic interactions, as described in Box 16.3, *Frightened of water*. Benzene rings also bind to other benzene rings or hydrocarbon chains by hydrophobic interactions.

Box 16.3 *Frightened of water*

If you have ever dropped oil onto water you may have noticed that, rather than spread out over the surface of the water, the oil tends to clump together, as shown in Figure 16.9. This is because oil and water do not mix. For example, if you shake vegetable oil and water together they are almost completely insoluble in each other. Globules of oil stay separate from the water and, if left, the mixture returns to two layers. The hydrocarbon chains that make up the

Figure 16.9 Oil drops on the surface of water.

oil do not contain any substantially charged atoms that can interact with the $\delta+$ and $\delta-$ charges on the water molecules, and so cannot disrupt the network of hydrogen bonds between the water molecules.

This incompatibility between water and oil means that the oil tries to expose to the water the smallest possible surface, which is a sphere. Such hydrocarbons are said to be hydrophobic, which means 'frightened of water'. This tendency for hydrocarbons to stick together in a charged environment is also observed in biological systems, where hydrocarbon groups try to align themselves next to each other. This is another form of intermolecular interaction, known as hydrophobic interaction, and its importance will become clearer in Block 9.

143

16.2.3 Drug specificity

Each of the intermolecular interactions described in Section 16.2.2 is relatively weak (from 3 to 10% of the strength of a covalent bond). One such interaction is not enough on its own to bind a messenger molecule in a receptor and stimulate a process. However, *if a drug is bound to a receptor by more than one intermolecular interaction*, it can be held tightly enough to stimulate a process.

● Look at the structure of adrenaline in Figure 16.6. What types of intermolecular interaction would bind adrenaline to a receptor?

○ The —OH and —NH— groups could bind via hydrogen bonding, and the benzene ring could bind by hydrophobic interaction.

Figure 16.10 shows one way in which adrenaline could bind to its receptor in more than one place. There are two types of interaction: hydrogen bonding and a hydrophobic interaction.

Figure 16.10   Possible binding of adrenaline to a receptor at three places. The dashed lines indicate hydrogen bonds, and there is a hydrophobic interaction between the benzene ring and the receptor surface, indicated by parallel lines.

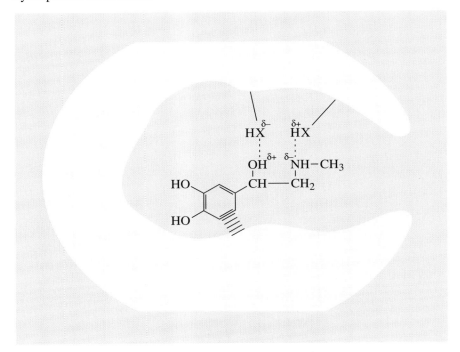

The requirement for more than one binding site puts very stringent constraints on the composition and shape of drug molecules. First, they must contain functional groups that can undergo the specific types of intermolecular interaction that match the groups on the receptor. Second, the binding points in the receptor occupy defined positions in three-dimensional space, and so the appropriate functional groups on the drug molecule need to match this geometric arrangement. However, the functional groups in a molecule can take up only certain fixed positions relative to each other, and these positions are limited by the overall structure. The net result is that only a few molecules will have the correct functional groups in the correct orientation to bind to a particular receptor.

Binding at more than one place ensures that only molecules with appropriate geometries and functional groups can fit the receptor.

Compounds **16.4**[W], **16.5**[W] and **16.6**[W] will not bind very well to the receptor in Figure 16.10. Compound **16.4** has only one point for hydrogen bonding, the amine group, rather than the two required. Compound **16.5** has two functional groups in the correct orientation, but one is a chloro group rather than an alcohol. Although the amine group can form a hydrogen bond with the receptor, the chloro group cannot undergo this interaction and so will not bind. Finally, compound **16.6** has the correct three groups but in the wrong positions in space relative to each other. Although one hydrogen bond is possible, say through the —OH group, the other functional group (—NH$_2$) will not be in the right place to form a second hydrogen bond with the receptor.

$CH_2-CH_2-NH-CH_3$

$\overset{\displaystyle Cl}{\underset{\displaystyle |}{}}$
$CH-CH_2-NH-CH_3$

OH

H_2N

16.4   **16.5**   **16.6**

It is no coincidence that the three compounds shown in Figure 16.6 have a common basic structure; after all, they bind to the same type of receptor. However, they do have slightly different structures and this is the source of their specificity. Salbutamol, for example, is similar enough to adrenaline that it binds to the receptors in the bronchial airways, but it is sufficiently different that it does not stimulate the receptors in the heart.

In this section we have seen how drugs bind to receptors through intermolecular interactions. In general, for a drug to be effective, it must have the correct shape so that it can fit the receptor and it must have appropriate functional groups in the right places (correctly disposed to each other in space) to ensure that it binds to the receptor in more than one place. Drugs can also bind to the active site of enzymes in a similar fashion and block their action. Discovering drugs with just the right structure may seem a tall order, but an understanding of drug action does allow new drugs to be made. This latter process demonstrates the true creativity of chemistry. A chemist can propose a new drug with a particular structure, but for testing this has to be made. Using the functional group approach, the required structure can be built up bit by bit until the new compound is formed. Most of these steps use organic compounds that have been obtained (via alkenes) from crude oil.

16.3 Summary of Section 16

1   Drugs work by affecting the action of enzymes or receptors that control the chemistry that goes on in the body. Both enzymes and receptors are biopolymers made from amino acids. Both have sites where drugs can bind. Drugs can either react with an enzyme and bind to it via covalent bonding and thus block its action, or bind to both enzymes and receptors via intermolecular interactions. Interactions at more than one place at this binding site not only ensure that the drug is bound tightly but also guarantee that only a few compounds will fit in the site and bind at the correct positions.

2   A hydrolysis reaction is the reverse of a condensation reaction and involves breaking a compound up with water.

3   A protein is a biopolymer made from monomers called amino acids.

16.7

O
||
CH₃—C—NH

OH

16.8

$$CH_3-CH_2-CH_2-\underset{\underset{NH_2}{|}}{CH}-\underset{\underset{O^-}{|}}{\overset{\overset{O}{\|}}{C}}$$

Question 16.3 Identify the functional groups in paracetamol (**16.7**)[W]. Again, assume for the purposes of this question that the benzene ring is not a functional group. Would you expect paracetamol to block the cyclo-oxygenase enzyme in the same way that aspirin (**16.2**) does? ◀

Question 16.4 An enzyme has an active site with the two functional groups shown in Figure 16.11. Describe the possible interactions between this active site and parts of the ion **16.8**. ◀

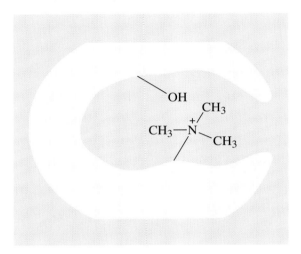

Figure 16.11 An active site on an enzyme.

Question 16.5 The ion **16.9** binds to a particular receptor. By looking at the functional groups and their disposition, identify which of the ions **16.10** to **16.12** are likely to fit the same receptor. ◀

16.9

$$CH_3-CH_2-CH_2-CH_2-\underset{\underset{O}{|}\underset{\underset{H}{\diagdown}}{}}{CH}-\underset{\underset{C=O}{|}\underset{\underset{O^-}{|}}{}}{CH_2}$$

16.10

$$CH_3-CH_2-CH_2-\underset{\underset{O}{|}\underset{\underset{H}{\diagdown}}{}}{CH}-\underset{\underset{C=O}{|}\underset{\underset{O^-}{|}}{}}{CH_2}$$

16.11

$$\underset{\underset{CH_2}{|}\underset{\underset{O}{|}}{}}{}-CH_2-CH_2-CH_2-CH_2-CH_2$$

16.12

$$CH_3-CH_2-CH_2-CH_2-\underset{\underset{O}{|}\underset{\underset{H}{\diagdown}}{}}{CH}-\underset{\underset{N(CH_3)_3}{|}\overset{+}{}}{CH_2}$$

Epilogue

In the last few sections we have described how crude oil is used as a fuel and to provide a feedstock for petrochemicals. We have also given you a flavour for how materials with specific properties are designed and made. As was pointed out earlier, crude oil is a valuable source of chemicals, and thus the search for alternative fuels is motivated not only by concern about the greenhouse effect. However, the reserves of crude oil are finite and when they run out it will be necessary to find alternative sources of chemical feedstocks.

○ Where do you think the best alternative source of feedstocks for polymers and drugs will be found?

○ For renewable sources we will have to depend on plants. In a sense we do this already because fossil fuels originated from plants.

The types of compound in plants are very different from those in crude oil and so it will be necessary to develop a whole new strategy as alternative feedstocks are developed. For example, fermentation of sugars using yeast leads to ethanol. This is how wine, beer and spirits are made. Distillation of the mixture leads to the isolation of pure ethanol. In fact ethanol is a good alternative to petrol (Activity 6.2). The internal combustion engine needs little modification to run on ethanol and so it has been used as a substitute for petrol in some countries that do not have their own sources of crude oil. However, in general, the use of ethanol is not as economic as the use of petrol.

Ethanol can also be used as a feedstock for the petrochemical industry, because under certain conditions it loses water to give ethene:

$$CH_3-CH_2-OH \longrightarrow CH_2{=}CH_2 + H_2O$$

The ethene can then be used to produce the many compounds shown in the picture on the title page.

The search for economic, sustainable, alternative feedstocks will provide many new challenges for chemists over the coming decades, but given the success over recent years in designing a huge variety of molecules for a wide range of applications, there is every reason to believe that this goal will be achieved.

Activity 17.1 The case for using alternative fuels

This activity builds on Activity 6.2. In it, you will criticize a written argument, and then produce a response to it. ◄

Activity 17.2 Reviewing your study of Block 8: transferability of skills

In this activity you will reflect on how well you have been able to transfer the skills developed in earlier blocks to the context of Block 8. ◄

Questions: answers and comments

Question 3.1 From Activity 3.1, the electron configurations of the Group II atoms are: beryllium, $1s^2 2s^2$; magnesium, $1s^2 2s^2 2p^6 3s^2$; calcium, $1s^2 2s^2 2p^6 3s^2 3p^6 4s^2$. These three atoms all have similar outer electron configurations of the type ns^2, where n is 2 for beryllium, 3 for magnesium and 4 for calcium. For the noble gas atoms, the electron configurations are: neon, $1s^2 2s^2 2p^6$; argon, $1s^2 2s^2 2p^6 3s^2 3p^6$. These both have similar outer electron configurations of the type $ns^2 np^6$, where n is 2 for neon and 3 for argon.

Question 3.2 As the principal quantum number is the number that precedes the letter in the sub-shell symbol, the values are 5, 4 and 3, respectively. The 5f sub-shell, like all f sub-shells, can hold a maximum of 14 electrons (see Figure 3.2). Likewise, the 4d sub-shell, like all d sub-shells, can hold 10, and the 3p sub-shell can hold six.

Question 3.3 The p, d and f sub-shells are the second, third and fourth sub-shells in a particular shell. But when $n = 1$, 2 and 3, there are only one, two and three sub-shells, respectively, in the shell. So 1p, 2d and 3f do not exist. By contrast, 4p is the second of four sub-shells in its shell, 5d is the third of five, and 6s is the first of six. So 4p, 5d and 6s sub-shells exist.

Question 3.4 Figure 3.3 shows that the first sub-shells to be filled, in order of increasing energy, are 1s, 2s, 2p, 3s and 3p. Of the six carbon electrons, the 1s and 2s sub-shells take two each, leaving two for the 2p sub-shell. Of the 14 silicon electrons, 1s and 2s take two each, 2p takes six before it is full, and two more then fill the 3s sub-shell. Twelve have now been accommodated, leaving two for 3p. So the carbon and silicon atoms have the electron configurations $1s^2 2s^2 2p^2$ and $1s^2 2s^2 2p^6 3s^2 3p^2$, respectively.

Both atoms have similar outer electron configurations of the type $ns^2 np^2$, where $n = 2$ for carbon and 3 for silicon. This is consistent with their appearance in the same group of the Periodic Table. As the outer configurations contain four electrons (two s and two p), this is consistent with Group IV.

Question 3.5 Tellurium is in Group VI, and Figure 3.9 shows that Group VI elements have the outer electron configuration $ns^2 np^4$. Tellurium is also in Period 5, so $n = 5$. Likewise, thallium is in Group III, with outer electron

configuration $ns^2 np^1$; as it occurs in Period 6, $n = 6$. Thus the outer electron configurations of the atoms are: tellurium, $5s^2 5p^4$; thallium, $6s^2 6p^1$. In both cases, the numbers of outer electrons (six and three, respectively) are equal to the group numbers.

Question 4.1 Structures **4.8–4.11** show the formulae. In each case, the number of lines issuing from each atom is equal to the element's quoted valency. Both alternatives for water tell us that each oxygen atom is connected to two hydrogens by two bonds, so either is satisfactory.

$$\text{H}-\text{Cl}$$

4. 8

$$\begin{array}{c} \text{H} \\ | \\ \text{H}-\text{C}-\text{H} \\ | \\ \text{H} \end{array}$$

4. 9

$$\begin{array}{c} \text{Cl} \\ | \\ \text{Cl}-\text{C}-\text{Cl} \\ | \\ \text{Cl} \end{array}$$

4. 10

$$\text{H}-\text{O}-\text{H} \quad or \quad \begin{array}{c} \text{H}-\text{O} \\ | \\ \text{H} \end{array}$$

4. 11

Question 4.2 (a) The crystal structure of lithium hydride is similar to that of sodium chloride in Figures 4.2 and 4.3: each lithium is surrounded by six hydrogens and each hydrogen by six lithiums. This is characteristic of an assembly of ions: each ion surrounds itself with ions of another type with an opposite charge.

(b) The alkali metal lithium is present as the ion Li^+; hence hydrogen is present as the hydride ion H^-. In Block 6 you saw that hydrogen can form an aqueous $H^+(aq)$ ion. Solids such as LiH show us that it can form an H^- ion as well.

(c) When molten lithium hydride is electrolysed, the negative hydride ions move to the positive electrode and become hydrogen gas, $H_2(g)$:

$$2H^-(\text{melt}) \longrightarrow H_2(g) + 2e^- \tag{4.5}$$

For every two hydride ions that react in this way, two positive lithium ions move to the negative electrode and become molten lithium metal:

$$2Li^+(\text{melt}) + 2e^- \longrightarrow 2Li(l) \tag{4.6}$$

Question 4.3 (a) The chains in Figure 4.8 show that hydrogen and fluorine atoms in solid HF are separated by either a shorter distance of 92 pm, or a longer distance of 157 pm. We take a hydrogen and fluorine atom separated by the short distance of 92 pm to be a discrete HF molecule. The shortest distance between two HF molecules is then 157 pm. Thus the structure of solid HF provides evidence that it is a molecular substance, and this is corroborated by the low melting and boiling temperatures (it is a liquid on a cold day), and its solubility in petrol.

(b) If HF is a molecular substance, liquid HF should be a poor conductor of electricity; this is the case.

Question 4.4 Structures **4.12–4.16** show the formulae. In each case, the number of lines issuing from each atom is equal to the element's quoted valency. Any arrangement that satisfies this condition is acceptable. For example, Cl—O—Cl is a satisfactory substitute for structure **4.13**.

$$O{=}O$$

4. 12

$$\begin{array}{c} Cl{-}O \\ | \\ Cl \end{array}$$

4. 13

$$\begin{array}{c} F \\ | \\ F{-}C{-}F \\ | \\ F \end{array}$$

4. 14

$$S{=}C{=}S$$

4.15

$$\begin{array}{c} Cl{-}C{-}Cl \\ \| \\ O \end{array}$$

4.16

Question 5.1 The shell structure of calcium is (2,8,8,2). Figure 5.2 reveals that loss of the two outer electrons from every calcium atom would give a Ca^{2+} ion with the shell structure of argon. If each of the two lost electrons is transferred to a chlorine atom, two Cl^- ions, also with the shell structure of argon, will be produced. When the ions are brought together in the ratio of one Ca^{2+} to two Cl^- ions, a neutral assembly will be formed. Thus the predicted empirical formula is $CaCl_2$.

Question 5.2 Nitrogen has the shell structure (2,5), with five outer electrons, and can attain the shell structure of the noble gas neon (2,8) by gaining three electrons, so the nitride ion is N^{3-}: it has a charge of 3–. Lithium and calcium have one and two outer electrons, respectively. By losing these, the atoms form the ions Li^+ and Ca^{2+} with the shell structures of helium and argon, respectively. The electrical neutrality of the compounds is ensured by combination in the ratios of three Li^+ ions to one N^{3-}, and of three Ca^{2+} ions to two N^{3-} ions. Thus the empirical formulae of lithium and calcium nitrides are Li_3N and Ca_3N_2, respectively.

Question 5.3 With six outer electrons each, the two oxygens in the O_2 molecule must form a double bond (two shared electron pairs, structure **5.8**) with each other if each is to attain a noble gas configuration; this agrees with the structural formula (structure **4.5**). SCl_2 contains single bonds (structure **5.9**).

$$\overset{..}{\underset{..}{O}} \overset{\times}{\underset{\times}{:}} \overset{+}{\underset{+}{O}}\overset{+}{}$$

5.8

$$:\overset{..}{\underset{..}{Cl}} \overset{\times\times}{\underset{\times}{:}} \overset{..}{\underset{..}{S}} \overset{\times}{\underset{\times}{}} \\ :\overset{..}{\underset{..}{Cl}}:$$

or

$$:\overset{..}{\underset{..}{Cl}} \overset{\times}{\underset{\times}{:}} S \overset{\times\times}{} \overset{..}{\underset{..}{:Cl}}:$$

5.9

In these Lewis structures, oxygen attains the neon configuration, and sulfur and chlorine the argon configuration. As with structural formulae, shape is unimportant; the important thing is to show the correct number of bonds (shared electron pairs) formed by each atom. As either form of structure **5.9** does this, both are acceptable.

Question 5.4 The molecular formulae are NH_3 and F_2, respectively. The structural formulae are shown as structures **5.10** and **5.11**, and the Lewis structures as structures **5.12** and **5.13**.

$$\begin{array}{c} H{-}N{-}H \\ | \\ H \end{array}$$

5.10

$$F{-}F$$

5.11

$$H \overset{\times\times}{\underset{\bullet\times}{:}} N \overset{\times}{:} H \\ \overset{\bullet}{\underset{H}{}}$$

5.12

$$:\overset{..}{\underset{..}{F}} \overset{\times\times}{\underset{\times\times}{:}} \overset{\times}{F}\overset{\times}{}$$

5.13

Question 5.5 The three ionic metallic hydrides will contain the hydride ion, H^-. The solid compounds NaH, MgH_2 and AlH_3 will then be electrically neutral only if they contain the positive ions Na^+, Mg^{2+} and Al^{3+}, respectively. The hydride ion has the electron structure of helium, and all the positive ions that of neon. The Lewis structures of the molecular hydrides are shown in structures **5.14–5.17**. Now there is electron sharing, but again, hydrogen attains the helium configuration; the other atoms in the hydrides, however, get the argon configuration.

$$\begin{array}{c} H \\ \bullet\times \\ H \overset{\bullet}{:} Si \overset{\times}{:} H \\ \times\bullet \\ H \end{array}$$

5.14

$$\begin{array}{c} \times\times \\ H \overset{\bullet}{:} P \overset{\times}{:} H \\ \bullet\times \\ H \end{array}$$

5.15

$$\begin{array}{c} \times\times \\ H \overset{\times}{:} S \overset{\times}{:} \\ \times\bullet \\ H \end{array}$$

5.16

$$\begin{array}{c} \times\times \\ H \overset{\times}{:} Cl \overset{\times}{:} \\ \times\times \end{array}$$

5.17

This question shows why there is the 1,2,3,4,3,2,1,0 valency pattern in the highest hydrides as one moves across the period. It arises from the need for the elements to achieve noble gas structures in either ionic compounds or molecular substances.

Question 5.6 The low melting and boiling temperatures of CCl_4 and OF_2 suggest that they are molecular substances. In the case of CCl_4, this is corroborated by the low conductivity of the liquid. For these molecules we can write the Lewis structures **5.18** and **5.19**.

5.18

5.19

K_2O is an ionic compound. This is apparent from its high melting temperature and its structure, in which each potassium is surrounded by oxygens, and each oxygen by potassiums. Such structures are consistent with the presence of ions. In K_2O, the ions K^+ and O^{2-} have the noble gas structures of argon and neon, respectively. Note that this gives the required electrical neutrality: two K^+ ions have a total charge that is exactly cancelled by that of one O^{2-} ion.

In agreement with point 5 of Section 5.6, the ionic compound is a combination of a metal from the left of the Periodic Table (potassium) with a non-metal from the right (oxygen). The covalent substances are combinations of non-metals.

Question 6.1 (a) As the question indicates, it is necessary to cool the injury. This can be achieved if an endothermic chemical reaction occurs in the pack; the area of injury becomes part of the surroundings and its temperature is lowered as the reaction absorbs energy in the form of heat. Since the solid is soluble, the chemical reaction that is taking place must be the dissolution of this solid in water. (A solid that is used in this type of cold pack is ammonium nitrate, NH_4NO_3.)

(b) A possible design for a hot pack would operate along the same lines, but would use a solid that gives rise to an exothermic reaction when it dissolves in water. (Of course the day must not be so cold that the water in the pack freezes before the pack is put into action!) In fact a hot pack based on calcium chloride, $CaCl_2$, has been marketed.

{It is important to note that the dissolution of solids in water can be either endothermic or exothermic. This is consistent with the idea that internal energy changes can result in the release or absorption of energy depending on the nature of a particular chemical reaction.}

Question 6.2 In the initial stages of an endothermic reaction, the temperature of the reaction mixture will be lowered. (You saw an example of this in the video sequence for the reaction shown in Figure 6.2.) However, with time, energy will flow in from the surroundings, until the products of the reaction are at the same temperature as the reactants were at the start. In these circumstances, all of the energy in the form of heat absorbed during the reaction will have been taken from the surroundings. This situation is then the same as if the reaction had occurred at constant temperature.

Question 6.3 As indicated in the question, it is first necessary to work out the mass of one mole of water molecules. The procedure for doing this was discussed in Block 6. We add together the relative atomic masses of the atoms in the formula unit and follow the number that is obtained by the symbol for the gram. For H_2O, adding the relative atomic masses gives: $[(2 \times 1.01) + 16.0]$, or 18.0 (to three significant figures). The mass of one mole of water molecules is 18.0 g.

We are also told that $\Delta H(vap) = +2\,260 \text{ kJ kg}^{-1}$.

So for 1 000 g of water the magnitude of the enthalpy change is 2 260 kJ.

For 1 g of water the magnitude of the enthalpy change is $\frac{2\,260}{1\,000}$ kJ.

Finally, for 18.0 g of water the magnitude of the enthalpy change is

$$\frac{2\,260 \times 18.0}{1\,000} \text{ kJ} = 40.7 \text{ kJ}$$

Hence, for one mole of water molecules, the magnitude of the enthalpy of vaporization is 40.7 kJ.

Question 6.4 When steam comes into contact with (relatively cold) skin, it will condense. This process is exothermic and so it will release heat {over 2 kJ per gram of water condensed}. This heat will raise the temperature of the skin. In addition, the condensed water, initially at 100 °C, will cool by transferring heat to the skin. There are thus two contributions that raise the temperature of the skin and this results in (painful) damage to the skin tissues.

Question 6.5 To carry out the calculation it is first necessary to find the molar mass of ethanol, C_2H_5OH: there are two carbon atoms, six hydrogen atoms and one oxygen atom in the molecule. Adding the relative atomic masses gives: $[(2 \times 12.0) + (6 \times 1.01) + 16.0]$, or 46.1 (to three significant figures).

The molar mass is thus 46.1 g. According to the thermochemical equation, the reaction of one mole of ethanol molecules, that is 46.1 g of ethanol, results in the release of 1 238 kJ of energy in the form of heat. So 1 g of ethanol will release $\frac{1238}{46.1}$ kJ.

If 1 kg (1 000 g) of liquid ethanol is fully burned in oxygen, then the energy released in the form of heat will be:

$$\frac{1238 \times 1000}{46.1} \, kJ = 27\,000 \, kJ$$

(The answer has been rounded to the nearest thousand kilojoules.)

A value of 27 000 can thus be entered in the last column of Table 6.1 as the value for ethanol.

{If you want further practice in this type of calculation, then check some of the other values in the final column of Table 6.1.}

Question 6.6   The reaction can be viewed as a two-step process:

step 1: $H_2(g) + Cl_2(g) \longrightarrow 2H(g) + 2Cl(g)$

step 2: $2H(g) + 2Cl(g) \longrightarrow 2HCl(g)$

Considering the bonds broken in step 1, there are 'one mole of hydrogen–hydrogen bonds' and 'one mole of chlorine–chlorine bonds'. Hence,

$\Delta H(\text{step 1}) = 436 \, kJ + 242 \, kJ$

$= +678 \, kJ$

Considering the bonds formed in step 2, there are 'two moles of hydrogen–chlorine bonds'. Hence,

$\Delta H(\text{step 2}) = 2 \times (-431 \, kJ)$

$= -862 \, kJ$

Thus, for the overall reaction,

$\Delta H = \Delta H(\text{step 1}) + \Delta H(\text{step 2})$

$= +678 \, kJ + (-862 \, kJ)$

$= +678 \, kJ - 862 \, kJ$

$= -184 \, kJ$

The enthalpy change is negative so the formation of HCl gas from hydrogen gas and chlorine gas is exothermic.

Question 7.1   The $\rightleftharpoons$ symbol indicates that the reaction goes in both directions. Oxygen molecules from the gas enter the solution, and oxygen molecules from the solution enter the gaseous state. At saturation the rates of the two processes are equal, and equilibrium is established.

Question 7.2   (a) The formula unit of sodium chloride is NaCl. The molar mass of sodium chloride is thus (23.0 + 35.5) g or 58.5 g.

20 g of sodium chloride contain $\frac{20}{58.5}$ mol or 0.34 mol (to two significant figures).

This amount is contained in one litre of solution, and so the concentration of sodium chloride is 0.34 mol litre^{-1}. Sodium chloride dissolves in water to give one sodium ion and one chloride ion for every formula unit of sodium chloride. Thus the concentration of Na$^+$(aq) is 0.34 mol litre^{-1}.

(b) The formula unit of calcium chloride is $CaCl_2$. The molar mass of calcium chloride is thus [(40.1 + (2 × 35.5)] g or 111.1 g.

30 g of calcium chloride contain $\frac{30}{111.1}$ mol or 0.27 mol.

This amount is contained in one litre of solution, and so the concentration of calcium chloride is 0.27 mol litre^{-1}. Calcium chloride dissolves in water to give one calcium ion and two chloride ions for every formula unit of calcium chloride; thus, the concentration of Cl$^-$(aq) is 2 × 0.27 mol litre^{-1} or 0.54 mol litre^{-1}.

Question 7.3   Extrapolating the curve drawn in Figure 7.5 to include the dihydride XH_2 suggests a value for its boiling temperature of around −70 °C. {However, as you will see shortly, extrapolating trends can be prone to problems. Interpolation is safer than extrapolation because there are points on either side of an estimate, suggesting a predictable variation. By definition, extrapolation involves moving into uncharted territory, where a predicted smooth change could be interrupted by new factors.}

Question 7.4   (a) Fluorine has the chemical formula F_2, thus the relative molecular mass is 2 × 19.0 = 38.0. Similarly chlorine, Cl_2, has a relative molecular mass of 2 × 35.5 = 71.0. Bromine, Br_2, has a relative molecular mass of 160 and iodine, I_2, has a relative molecular mass of 254.

(b) The London interactions between the molecules will increase with an increase in relative molecular mass, that is in the order F_2, Cl_2, Br_2, I_2. The stronger the attractive interactions between molecules the greater the energy that is required to overcome these interactions and hence the higher the boiling temperature. The boiling temperatures, therefore, will also increase in the order of relative molecular mass. {This trend is observed in practice, as shown in Table 7.1. The column of melting temperatures is relevant to Question 7.6.}

Table 7.1 The boiling and melting temperatures of the halogens.

Halogen	Boiling temperature/°C	Melting temperature/°C
F_2	−188	−220
Cl_2	−35	−101
Br_2	59	−7
I_2	184	114

Question 7.5 (a) If London interactions are the only intermolecular interactions between the molecules, then on the basis of relative molecular mass these will be larger between the ethane molecules, so ethane should have a higher boiling temperature than methane. This is confirmed in Table 7.2.

(b) The only attractive interactions between hydrogen molecules are London interactions, whereas hydrogen fluoride molecules can also form hydrogen bonds. Hydrogen fluoride has a larger relative molecular mass than hydrogen. Hence, London interactions between hydrogen fluoride molecules will be greater than those between hydrogen molecules. The presence of hydrogen bonding will also mean that there are additional intermolecular interactions between hydrogen fluoride molecules. Thus hydrogen fluoride should have the higher boiling temperature, as confirmed in Table 7.2.

Table 7.2 The boiling temperatures of the compounds in Question 7.5.

Compound	Boiling temperature/°C
ethane	−89
methane	−164
hydrogen	−253
hydrogen fluoride	20

Question 7.6 Melting involves overcoming the attractive interactions that hold atoms, ions or molecules together in the solid state. The stronger the attractive interactions, then the greater the energy that is required to overcome these attractive interactions and as a consequence the solid melts at a higher temperature.

The relative molecular mass, and hence the magnitude of London interactions, increases as we go from fluorine to iodine. Thus the melting temperatures of the solid forms of these halogens should increase in the same order, as is found in practice.

Question 7.7 On the basis of London interactions alone, the melting temperature would be expected to increase in a regular way from NH_3 to BiH_3, that is, to increase with increasing relative molecular mass. However, Figure 7.7 shows that hydrogen bonding is possible between ammonia molecules, NH_3. So with ammonia there is an additional attractive interaction, which should result in the melting temperature of ammonia being higher than that expected on the basis of considering London interactions alone. In fact the melting temperature of ammonia is −78 °C whereas that of PH_3 is −134 °C.

Question 7.8 (a) Because sulfuric acid is a strong acid, when it dissolves in water it completely dissociates into ions. Equation 7.7 shows that two hydrogen ions are formed for every molecule of sulfuric acid. Thus a 0.1 mol litre^{-1} solution of sulfuric acid has a hydrogen ion concentration of 0.2 mol litre^{-1}.

(b) Because hydrogen cyanide is a weak acid, when it dissolves in water it only partially dissociates. Unfortunately the question does not tell us to what extent it breaks down into ions; however, we can say that the hydrogen ion concentration will be less than 1.0 mol litre^{-1}.

Question 8.1 There are four moles of product molecules and two moles of reactant molecules. If the operating pressure is increased then the composition of the equilibrium mixture will change so that the proportion of reactants increases. Hence increasing the pressure would actually *decrease* the equilibrium yield of hydrogen cyanide.

Question 8.2 The equilibrium yield of nitrogen monoxide will increase with increasing temperature because the forward direction of the reaction is endothermic. Thus the yield will be greater at 500 °C than at room temperature.

Question 8.3   The equilibrium expression will be:

$$K = \frac{[H^+(aq)][NO_2^-(aq)]}{[HNO_2(aq)]}$$

The equilibrium constant at 25 °C can be calculated for all three solutions. Thus, for example, for solution A:

$$K = \frac{(6.2 \times 10^{-3}\,mol\,litre^{-1}) \times (6.2 \times 10^{-3}\,mol\,litre^{-1})}{0.090\,mol\,litre^{-1}}$$

$$= 4.3 \times 10^{-4}\,mol\,litre^{-1}\ \text{(to 2 sig figs)}$$

Similar calculations for solutions B and C give the same value of K. Thus the value for the equilibrium constant at 25 °C is 4.3×10^{-4} mol litre^{-1}. The magnitude of this quantity is clearly the same for all three equilibrium mixtures.

Question 8.4   We have treated this question as a 'problem' and in this answer we have used the strategy developed in Activity 8.2, even though the question did not specifically ask for this. Remember that your strategy can be applied to any question and will be especially useful if you are initially not sure how to tackle the question.

(a) *First think about what you already know, and how you are going to find the answer.*

For the dissociation of iodic acid in water, we know that the equilibrium expression is:

$$K = \frac{[H^+(aq)][IO_3^-(aq)]}{[HIO_3(aq)]} \qquad (8.26)$$

Values for [H$^+$(aq)], [IO$_3^-$(aq)] and [HIO$_3$(aq)] are given in Table 8.2 for both 25 °C and 45 °C, so to find K at each of these temperatures we just need to substitute these values in Equation 8.26.

Now do the calculation.

Using the information from Table 8.2,

at 25 °C,

$$K = \frac{(0.071\,mol\,litre^{-1}) \times (0.071\,mol\,litre^{-1})}{0.029\,mol\,litre^{-1}}$$

$$= 0.17\,mol\,litre^{-1}$$

(to 2 sig figs)

and at 45 °C,

$$K = \frac{(0.066\,mol\,litre^{-1}) \times (0.066\,mol\,litre^{-1})}{0.034\,mol\,litre^{-1}}$$

$$= 0.13\,mol\,litre^{-1}$$

(to 2 sig figs)

Does the answer seem reasonable?

The unit of K turns out to be mol litre^{-1} as expected. It is difficult to say if the numerical values are reasonable, but they are certainly consistent with the numbers in Table 8.2. The decrease in K between 25 °C and 45 °C is consistent with the reduction in the concentration of products and the increase in the concentration of the reactant.

(b) *First think about what you already know, and how you are going to find the answer.*

We have calculated the equilibrium constant at two temperatures in part (a) and we will use the way that K depends on temperature to determine whether the reaction is exothermic or endothermic.

Now do the calculation.

There is a decrease in the magnitude of the equilibrium constant K for the reaction as the temperature is raised. This is the way that K for any exothermic reaction depends on temperature, so the dissociation of iodic acid must be an exothermic reaction.

Does the answer seem reasonable?

We can check this answer by seeing whether it is consistent with Le Chatelier's principle. The molar concentrations in Table 8.2 indicate that the equilibrium position moves to the left as the temperature is raised. According to Le Chatelier's principle this would be consistent with the dissociation reaction being exothermic in the forward direction, which is the answer we reached by considering how K changed with temperature.

Question 8.5   The carbon dioxide gas produced by decaying organic matter causes the local concentration of this gas to be larger underground than at the surface. This results in more gas being dissolved in underground water. Because the dissolution of carbon dioxide gas in water is exothermic, the lower temperatures underground also lead to more gas being dissolved.

Question 9.1   (a) Sodium hydroxide dissociates completely in water to give Na$^+$(aq) and OH$^-$(aq) ions. Thus in a NaOH solution of concentration 1.0×10^{-2} mol litre^{-1}, it follows that [OH$^-$(aq)] $= 1.0 \times 10^{-2}$ mol litre^{-1}. At 25 °C, the corresponding hydrogen ion concentration will be [H$^+$(aq)] $= 1.0 \times 10^{-12}$ mol litre^{-1}. The solution, as expected, is basic because the hydrogen ion concentration is less than 1.0×10^{-7} mol litre^{-1} (Figure 9.1).

(b) Hydrochloric acid is a strong acid. Thus, a 1.0×10^{-5} mol litre^{-1} solution of HCl will have [H$^+$(aq)] $= 1.0 \times 10^{-5}$ mol litre^{-1}. The solution is acidic because the hydrogen ion concentration is greater than 1.0×10^{-7} mol litre^{-1}, at 25 °C.

(c) NaCl dissolves to give only Na$^+$(aq) and Cl$^-$(aq) ions. Thus the concentration of hydrogen ions will not be affected and will remain at that for neutral water; [H$^+$(aq)] $= 1.0 \times 10^{-7}$ mol litre^{-1} at 25 °C.

(d) Acetic acid is a weak acid and will only partially dissociate into ions in water. Thus a 1.0 mol litre^{-1} solution of HAc will have a hydrogen ion concentration greater than 1.0×10^{-7} mol litre^{-1}, but less than 1.0 mol litre^{-1}. At 25 °C, [H$^+$(aq)] $= 4.2 \times 10^{-3}$ mol litre^{-} (Section 8.3.2). The solution is acidic.

Question 9.2 (a) Mixing one litre of a 1.0 mol litre^{-1} hydrochloric acid solution with one litre of a 1.0 mol litre^{-1} sodium hydroxide solution is effectively carrying out a neutralization reaction:

$$HCl(aq) + NaOH(aq) \rightleftharpoons NaCl(aq) + H_2O(l)$$

or

$$H^+(aq) + OH^-(aq) \rightleftharpoons H_2O(l)$$

The hydrogen ion concentration that results will be that for pure water, that is [H$^+$(aq)] $= 1.0 \times 10^{-7}$ mol litre^{-1} at 25 °C.

(b) Mixing two litres of a 1.0 mol litre^{-1} hydrochloric acid solution with one litre of a 1.0 mol litre^{-1} solution of sodium hydroxide is effectively mixing 2.0 mol of H$^+$(aq) with 1.0 mol of OH$^-$(aq). Neutralization occurs, but 1.0 mol of H$^+$(aq) is 'left over'. The total volume after mixing can be assumed to be 3.0 litres and so the final hydrogen ion concentration is 1.0 mol in 3.0 litres, that is 0.33 mol litre^{-1}.

Question 9.3 (a) A 1.0×10^{-2} mol litre^{-1} solution of NaOH has a hydrogen ion concentration of 1.0×10^{-12} mol litre^{-1}, thus it has a pH of 12. This is greater than 7, as expected for a basic solution.

(b) A 1.0×10^{-5} mol litre^{-1} solution of HCl has a hydrogen ion concentration of 1.0×10^{-5} mol litre^{-1}, thus it has a pH of 5. This is less than 7, as expected for an acidic solution.

(c) A 1.0×10^{-3} mol litre^{-1} solution of NaCl is neutral, with a pH of 7.

Question 10.1 In the equation for this reaction there are ten moles of product molecules (4 + 6) and nine moles of reactant molecules (4 + 5). Increasing the pressure therefore leads to a decrease in the equilibrium yield of nitrogen monoxide. The fact that a high pressure *is* employed suggests that this increases the rate of reaction.

{In an industrial reaction like this there is another factor, which we have not considered, that can lead to the reaction being operated at high pressure. This is the need to reduce the volume of the plant. A higher pressure enables more moles of reactant to be contained within a given volume.}

Question 10.2 The diagram is shown in Figure 10.8. Because the reaction is exothermic (ΔH is negative), the internal energy of the products is lower than that of the reactants.

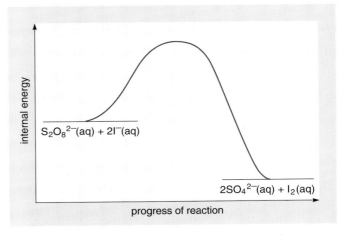

Figure 10.8 A schematic representation of how the internal energy changes during the reaction in Equation 10.1.

Question 10.3 Because ΔH is negative, this reaction is exothermic in the forward direction, so the equilibrium yield of sulfur trioxide at 500 °C will be *less* than that at room temperature. It is likely that a high temperature is used to ensure a reasonable rate of reaction.

Question 10.4 (a) The diagram is shown in Figure 10.9.

(b) (i) Raising the temperature would increase the yield because the reaction is endothermic in the forward direction (Section 8).

(ii) There are four moles of product molecules and two moles of reactant molecules and therefore increasing the pressure would decrease the yield (Section 8).

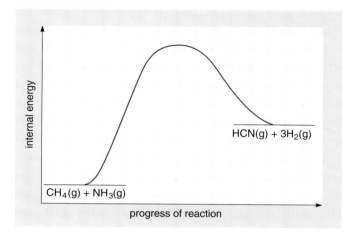

Figure 10.9   A schematic representation of how the internal energy changes during the production of hydrogen cyanide.

(iii) A catalyst does not affect the composition of the equilibrium mixture. It will therefore not change the equilibrium yield.

Question 10.5   (a) Reaction 10.5 is exothermic in the forward direction, and so increasing the temperature of the exhaust gases will decrease the equilibrium yield of nitrogen.

(b) Both the raised temperature and the catalyst increase the rate of reaction 10.5.

(c) The catalyst increases the rate of reaction 10.5 so that by the time the exhaust gases reach the atmosphere, the reaction is virtually complete. Reaction 10.7 does not then occur.

Question 11.1   Plants can use carbon in the most abundant chemical form found in the atmosphere — carbon dioxide. Under the action of sunlight, green vegetation absorbs this gas and converts it into sugars in the process of photosynthesis (Blocks 2 and 4).

Question 11.2   The reaction is endothermic in the forward direction. Thus, increasing the temperature will increase the equilibrium yield of hydrogen. The high operating temperature of 750 °C, and the presence of the nickel catalyst, will favour a fast reaction. Thus, a high temperature increases both the equilibrium yield and the rate of reaction; there is no conflict.

There are two moles of reactant molecules and four moles of product molecules. Thus, increasing the pressure will mean that the equilibrium yield of hydrogen will decrease; this does not seem to be ideal. {However, working at a higher pressure may increase the rate of reaction and, in addition, it will allow a more compact plant to be operated.}

Question 12.1   Four hydrogens need to be attached to one carbon to satisfy all the valencies. This gives a compound with molecular formula CH_4.

Carbon has the shell structure (2,4), with four outer electrons. It can attain the shell structure of the noble gas neon (2,8) by gaining four electrons from four shared electron pairs (covalent bonds). Hydrogen has only one electron (1), so to attain the shell structure of helium (2) it gains one electron from one shared electron pair.

$$
\begin{array}{c}
H \\
\overset{\bullet\,\times}{} \\
H \overset{\times}{\bullet}\, C \overset{\times}{\bullet}\, H \\
\overset{\times\,\bullet}{} \\
H
\end{array}
$$

{This compound, which you have met in earlier blocks, is called methane. It is the major constituent of natural gas and is also the 'marsh gas' produced by rotting vegetation.}

Question 12.2   Figure 12.7 shows the stages in drawing the structures of ethane and pentane. The carbon chain is drawn first, then bonds are added so that each carbon has four (to satisfy its valency), and finally hydrogens are added.

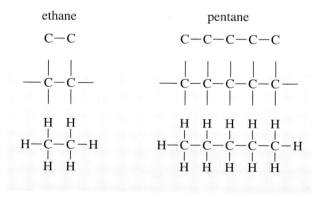

Figure 12.7   The three stages in drawing the structural formulae of ethane and pentane.

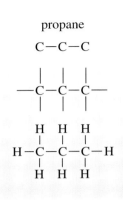

propane

C—C—C

Figure 12.8
The three stages in drawing the structural formula of propane.

Question 12.3   Figure 12.8 shows the various stages. The structural formula shows that propane has the molecular formula C_3H_8.

Question 12.4   **12.9** is a branched-chain alkane. There is a linear chain of eight carbon atoms, with a one carbon atom branch attached to the third carbon from the left.

12.10 is a cycloalkane. The chain of four carbon atoms is arranged in a ring.

12.11 is not an alkane. As well as hydrogen and carbon atoms it contains a fluorine atom.

12.12 is a linear-chain alkane. There is a linear chain of six carbon atoms.

Question 12.5   **12.14** is a linear-chain alkane. The carbons are joined to each other by single bonds, in a linear fashion.

12.15 is an aromatic compound. It contains a ring of six carbon atoms joined by alternating single and double bonds.

12.16 is another linear-chain alkane. Even though it is drawn in a bent fashion, the carbons are joined to each other by single bonds, one after the other.

12.17 is a branched-chain alkane. There is a row of linked carbon atoms with a branch attached to the second carbon from the right.

Question 12.6   **12.18** and **12.20** have correct structural formulae. Each carbon has four bonds attached to it and each hydrogen is attached by one bond. Thus all the valencies are satisfied. **12.19** has an incorrect structural formula: the central carbon has only three bonds attached to it.

Question 12.7 (a)

$$CH_3-CH_2-CH_2-CH_2-CH_2-CH_2-CH_2-CH_3$$

(b)

$$\begin{array}{cc} CH_2-CH_2 \\ | \qquad | \\ CH_2-CH_2 \end{array}$$

(c) Drawing the abbreviated structural formula for C_4H_{10} may have given you some problems if you did not realize that bonds in abbreviated structural formulae can go in any direction, including up or down if there is no other place to draw them. The important point is to have the right number of bonds to each carbon — four:

$$CH_3-\underset{\underset{CH_3}{|}}{CH}-CH_3$$

(d)

$$\begin{array}{cc} CH_3 \\ | \\ CH_2-CH \\ | \qquad | \\ CH_2-CH_2 \end{array}$$

If the molecule contains a ring of four carbons, the molecular formula indicates there must be another carbon atom. This is a one carbon atom branch. It can come off any of the four carbons in the ring because they are all equivalent.

Question 12.8   Isomerization implies a process in which the product is an isomer of the reactant. For example, hexane can be converted into a branched-chain alkane with the same molecular formula:

$$CH_3-CH_2-CH_2-CH_2-CH_2-CH_3$$
$$\downarrow$$
$$CH_3-\underset{\underset{CH_3}{|}}{CH}-CH_2-CH_2-CH_3$$

Table 12.2 shows that branched-chain alkanes have much higher octane numbers than linear-chain alkanes. In fact, a range of branched-chain isomers of pentane and hexane can be formed. {This process is carried out at 100–200 °C using a platinum catalyst.}

Question 14.1 If we replace the CH_3 by an R group in Equation 14.13 we get the generalized reaction for the reduction of a carboxylic acid to an alcohol:

$$R-COOH \xrightarrow{H_2/catalyst} R-CH_2-OH$$

This reflects the fact that only the functional group undergoes change in the reaction and not the hydrocarbon group. In benzoic acid, R is a benzene ring, thus replacement of the R group by a benzene ring in the generalized equation gives:

Question 14.2 (a) This contains an alcohol group, written as HO—, and a carboxylic acid group, —COOH. {As you will see in the next section this compound is used to make a polyester.}

(b) This contains a carbon–carbon double bond, so it is an alkene. It also contains an ester group.

Question 14.3 The Lewis structure of ethanol is:

The oxygen atom has two pairs of non-bonded electrons, shown as crosses.

Question 14.4 The strategy we developed in Activity 14.5 was (i) identify the functional group, (ii) look up the reactions of this functional group, and (iii) identify the hydrocarbon portions of the reactants that do not change and copy them to give the product.

(a) The reactant is an alcohol. Potassium dichromate ($K_2Cr_2O_7$) in hydrochloric acid oxidizes an alcohol to give a carboxylic acid. The generalized equation for this is given by Equation 14.12. In this case, the R group in the reactant alcohol is CH_3-CH_2-, thus substituting this for R in the product in Equation 14.12 gives CH_3-CH_2-COOH.

(b) In this reaction there are two reactants, a carboxylic acid and an alcohol. The only way that these two groups

react together is via a condensation reaction to give an ester. The generalized equation is given in the Appendix in the Study File. Because there are two reactants we have to make sure we do not get the R groups mixed up, so we label them R^1 and R^2. R^1 comes from the carboxylic acid, so R^1 is CH_3-CH_2-, and R^2 comes from the alcohol, so is $CH_3-CH_2-CH_2-CH_2-$. Substituting these groups in the generalized equation gives the product:

(c) The third reaction involves an alkene. The only reaction you have learnt for alkenes is an addition reaction. In this case water is added across the double bond. In terms of the general addition reaction given in the Study File, X = H and Y = OH, and R^1 is CH_3- and R^2 is $-CH_3$, giving the product:

Question 14.5 Leaf alcohol contains two functional groups, an alkene functional group and an alcohol functional group:

Each functional group will undergo characteristic reactions. Alcohols undergo oxidation to a carboxylic acid or reaction with a carboxylic acid to give an ester. Alkenes undergo addition reactions.

(a) This reaction is a condensation reaction between the alcohol functional group of leaf alcohol and the carboxylic acid to give an ester. The generalized reaction is given in the Study File. Here R^1 comes from the carboxylic acid, so R^1 is CH_3, and R^2 comes from leaf alcohol, so is $CH_3-CH_2-CH=CH-CH_2-CH_2-$. Substituting these groups in the generalized equation gives the product:

(b) This reaction is an addition reaction. Equation 13.2 shows that bromine adds across the double bond. The generalized addition reaction is given in the Study File, and in this case X and Y are both Br. Also, R^1 is

$CH_3—CH_2—$ and R^2 is $—CH_2—CH_2—OH$ so the product is

$$CH_3-CH_2-\overset{\overset{\displaystyle Br}{|}}{CH}-\overset{\overset{\displaystyle Br}{|}}{CH}-CH_2-CH_2-OH$$

{Note that R^2 contains another functional group, OH, which does not react; in this case, R^2 represents 'the rest of the molecule'.}

Question 14.6 (a) In this reaction the alcohol gains oxygen and loses hydrogen. It is oxidized.

(b) In this reaction, which is an addition reaction, the alkene gains hydrogen so is reduced. In this case there is no accompanying loss of oxygen.

Question 15.1 The first two of these reactions involve an amine and a carboxylic acid. The question tells us that they undergo a condensation reaction, and so the product must be an amide.

(a) The amine has only one R group and so Equation 15.2 is the most appropriate. R^1 comes from the carboxylic acid and is $CH_3—$, R^2 comes from the amine and is also $CH_3—$, giving:

$$CH_3-\overset{\overset{\displaystyle O}{\|}}{\underset{\underset{\displaystyle NH-CH_3}{}}{C}}$$

(b) There are two groups on the amine and so Equation 15.3 is more appropriate. In this case R^1 is $CH_3—CH_2—$ and R^2 and R^3 are $CH_3—$, and the product is

$$CH_3-CH_2-\overset{\overset{\displaystyle O}{\|}}{\underset{\underset{\underset{\displaystyle CH_3}{|}}{N-CH_3}}{C}}$$

(c) This involves an amine reacting with hydrochloric acid. As we saw in Equation 15.1, an amine is basic and will react with an acid to give an ammonium salt. In this case R is $CH_3—CH_2—$:

$$CH_3-CH_2-NH_2 + HCl \rightleftharpoons CH_3-CH_2-NH_3^+ + Cl^-$$

{As a result of their acidic nature, carboxylic acids also react with amines at room temperature to give ammonium salts and carboxylate ions:

$$R^1-NH_2 + R^2-\overset{\overset{\displaystyle O}{\|}}{\underset{\underset{\displaystyle OH}{}}{C}} \longrightarrow R^1-\overset{+}{NH_3} + R^2-\overset{\overset{\displaystyle O}{\|}}{\underset{\underset{\displaystyle O^-}{}}{C}}$$

However, when heated, they undergo the condensation reaction described in parts (a) and (b).}

Question 15.2 (a)(i) This addition polymer is formed by linking many $CH_2{=}CHCl$ monomers together. In so doing, one of the bonds in the carbon–carbon double bond is broken to form two new bonds, giving the monomer unit:

$$-CH_2-\overset{\overset{\overset{\displaystyle Cl}{|}}{}}{CH}-$$

(a)(ii) This condensation polymer is formed by a condensation reaction occurring at each of the functional groups in the monomer, the alcohol and the carboxylic acid groups. The new bond is formed between the oxygen of the alcohol and the carbon of the carboxylic acid, thus the monomer unit is:

$$-\overset{\overset{\displaystyle O}{\|}}{C}-CH_2-CH_2-CH_2-O-$$

(b) This is an addition polymer, formed from an alkene. The monomer therefore contains a carbon–carbon double bond:

$$\overset{\displaystyle O\diagdown}{\underset{\underset{\displaystyle CH{=}CH_2}{|}}{C}}{\diagup}^{\displaystyle OH}$$

Question 15.3 (a) The first polymer is an addition polymer, and so its monomer must be an alkene. Thus the monomer unit must have a two-carbon repeating unit in the backbone, and the monomer must contain a $C{=}C$ double bond:

$$-\overset{\overset{\overset{\displaystyle CH_3}{|}}{}}{CH}-CH_2- \qquad \overset{\overset{\overset{\displaystyle CH_3}{|}}{}}{CH}{=}CH_2$$

monomer unit   monomer

(b) This is a condensation polymer containing many amide groups. Thus, its monomer must contain an amine and a carboxylic acid. When the amide is formed, a bond is made between the nitrogen of the amine and the carbon of the carboxylic acid. Thus, the monomer unit and monomer are:

$$-\overset{\overset{\displaystyle O}{\|}}{C}-CH_2-CH_2-NH- \qquad HO-\overset{\overset{\displaystyle O}{\|}}{C}-CH_2-CH_2-NH_2$$

monomer unit   monomer

Question 15.4   No. In each case only two amide links could be formed to give condensation products as shown, with a molecule of water being eliminated at each stage.

(a)

$$CH_3-\overset{\overset{\displaystyle O}{\|}}{C}-OH \ + \ H_2N-(CH_2)_6-NH_2$$

$$\downarrow -H_2O$$

$$CH_3-\overset{\overset{\displaystyle O}{\|}}{C}-NH-(CH_2)_6-NH_2 \ + \ HO-\overset{\overset{\displaystyle O}{\|}}{C}-CH_3$$

$$\downarrow -H_2O$$

$$CH_3-\overset{\overset{\displaystyle O}{\|}}{C}-NH-(CH_2)_6-NH-\overset{\overset{\displaystyle O}{\|}}{C}-CH_3$$

(b)

$$CH_3-NH_2 \ + \ HO-\overset{\overset{\displaystyle O}{\|}}{C}-(CH_2)_4-\overset{\overset{\displaystyle O}{\|}}{C}-OH$$

$$\downarrow -H_2O$$

$$CH_3-NH-\overset{\overset{\displaystyle O}{\|}}{C}-(CH_2)_4-\overset{\overset{\displaystyle O}{\|}}{C}-OH \ + \ H_2N-CH_3$$

$$\downarrow -H_2O$$

$$CH_3-NH-\overset{\overset{\displaystyle O}{\|}}{C}-(CH_2)_4-\overset{\overset{\displaystyle O}{\|}}{C}-NH-CH_3$$

However, these products do not contain functional groups that could react further with other monomers or with other products. So the presence of two functional groups in *both* of the reactants is necessary if a polymer is to be formed.

Question 15.5   The addition polymer formed by linking together tetrafluoroethene monomers is:

$$-CF_2-CF_2-CF_2-CF_2-CF_2-CF_2-CF_2-CF_2-$$

Question 16.1   In salicylic acid we can identify an alcohol and a carboxylic acid functional group:

In this compound there are no linear chains of carbon atoms. However, the benzene ring provides the framework on which to hang the other functional groups. In salicylic acid, the alcohol and carboxylic acid groups are attached to adjacent carbon atoms. All the other atoms are hydrogen atoms.

Question 16.2   (a) This is the hydrolysis of an ester, and so the products are a carboxylic acid and an alcohol:

$$R^1-COOH + HO-CH_3$$

(b) This is the hydrolysis of an amide, and so the products are a carboxylic acid and an amine:

$$R^1-COOH + H_2N-CH_2-CH_3$$

Question 16.3   The functional groups in paracetamol are highlighted — an alcohol group and an amide group:

The shape of the paracetamol molecule is very different from that of the aspirin molecule, and it does not contain an ester group that could react with an —OH group in the active site. Hence, we would not expect it to block the cyclo-oxygenase enzyme in the same way that aspirin does. {Paracetamol binds to another part of the cyclo-oxygenase enzyme via intermolecular interactions and thus blocks its action. This is why paracetamol has a similar effect to that of aspirin.}

Question 16.4   The first step is to look for particular functional groups; we can split the ion **16.8** into a number of imaginary parts, an amine group, a carboxylate group and a saturated hydrocarbon chain:

The nitrogen of the amine, NH_2, is able to form a hydrogen bond with a hydrogen attached to an electronegative atom, such as that found in the alcohol group on the receptor. Alternatively the hydrogen attached to the nitrogen of the amine can form a hydrogen bond with the oxygen of the alcohol group.

The carboxylate group bears a full negative charge and is therefore likely to form an ionic interaction with the positively charged ammonium group on the active site.

159

Question 16.5 First we need to identify the types of binding that **16.9** would undergo. The hydrocarbon chain could be attracted by hydrophobic interactions, the alcohol group could form a hydrogen bond, and the negatively charged carboxylate group could undergo an ionic interaction with a positively charged group. But, remember, the groups need to be in the correct places.

The ion **16.10** has one $-CH_2-$ group fewer than the ion **16.9**, but it would be expected to bind to the same receptor because it contains the same functional groups in the same places. The loss of one $-CH_2-$ group would have only a minor effect on the hydrophobic interactions of the hydrocarbon group.

The ion **16.11** will not bind. Although it has the correct groups, they are not in the right spatial orientation; in **16.9** they are close together whereas in **16.11** they are far apart.

The ion **16.12** will not bind. The functional groups are in the correct places, but the negatively charged group has been replaced by a positively charged one. The negatively charged group in the ion **16.9** would bind with a positively charged group on the receptor, but the latter group would repel the positively charged group in **16.12**.

Acknowledgements

Grateful acknowledgement is made to the following sources for permission to reproduce material in this unit:

Figure 5.3: University of California Archives; *Figure 11.2*: Reproduced courtesy of the Library and Information Centre, Royal Society of Chemistry; *Figure 11.3*: © The Nobel Foundation, supplied by the Royal Society of Chemistry; *Figures 12.2 and 12.3*: Photographs courtesy of Minton, Treharne and Davies Ltd; *Figure 16.1*: Wellcome Institute Library, London.

Index

Entries and page numbers in **bold type** refer to key words which are printed in **bold** in the text and which are defined in the Glossary. These are terms that we expect you to be able to explain the meaning of, and use correctly, both during and at the end of the course. An entry followed by ^{G} indicates a term which is defined in the Glossary but which is not bold in the text. Where the page number is given in *italics*, the indexed information is carried mainly or wholly in an illustration or table. Section summaries and answers to questions are not indexed.